The Iron Heart of Gwent

by Clive Davies & Gwyn Tilley

Acknowledgements

During the writing of this book, the authors accessed many sources of information on both the mining and iron industries.

Among the sources we wish to thank are:

The staff at The County Record Office, Croesyceiliog, for their willing help.

Sir Richard Hanbury Tenison KCVO and the ever courteous staff at the Park Estate Office, Pontypool, for maps, information, etc.

The staff at Torfaen Museum Trust, for their help in our research, and permission to use certain photographs.

The engravings are from contemporary newspapers, mainly *The Graphic* and the *Illustrated London News*.

Susan and Colin Cook for the use of their computer skills.

Mr Jack Tenison, Mr Adrian Fawcett, Mr Wayne Perham, son David, and brother Ian (mining group).

Councillor Neil Waite, for his help and patience as a guide to the Blaendare area.

Mr Terry Targett for information, photographs, and his time.

Mr David Boddington who is ever ready to help for photographs, information, etc.

Mr Richard Roynon, for his special effort in finding photographs and information.

Mr and Mrs K Bones for photographs and information.

Mr Brian Foster for the use of text quoted from his book.

Mr Brian Roden for photographs and advice.

Mr Brian Stevens, mining surveyor, also for information.

The late Mr Robert Bendall for photographs and information.

Mr John Thickins for photographs and information.

And last but not least our long-suffering wives.

The Iron Heart of Gwent

by Clive Davies & Gwyn Tilley

Landmark Publishing

Published by

Ashbourne Hall, Cokayne Ave
Ashbourne, Derbyshire DE6 1EJ England
Tel: (01335) 347349 Fax: (01335) 347303
e-mail: landmark@clara.net
web site: www.landmarkpublishing.co.uk

1st Edition

13 ISBN: 978-1-84306-401-5

10 ISBN: 1-84306-401-4

Print: Cromwell Press, Trowbridge, Wiltshire

Design by: Sarah Labuhn

Cover photo front: The British Iron Works
Cover photo back top: Weir Sluices on the Afonllwyd River
Cover photo back bottom: Osborne Forge

Contents

"How many a man has dated a new era in his life from the reading of a book"
Henry David Thoreau. 1817–1862

Chapter 1. Pontypool

When one looks at Pontypool today, it is hard to imagine that in times gone by, much of the surrounding area suffered such an upheaval to the land that it left its landscapes looking like World War I battlefields. Fortunately, the bulldozer has now returned many places to something like what it would have once looked like, and apart from a few areas where the greenery hides what were once colliery waste tips, then in general, much of what the eye sees today is a vast improvement, and indeed, it is a credit to the local councils and the willingness of present day landowners to have spent money in this manner, in an attempt to clean up the land, which after all is the land we all have to live in, but we should also remember that this same bulldozer also removed many of the vestiges of our heritage, something which was against the wishes of many local people.

Pontypool is bounded on the north by Abersychan, on the south by Cwmbran and Newport, while to the east is Usk, and to the west lies Crumlin.

It is said that Pontypool had taken its name from a clergyman, David ap Howell (David, son of Howell) who built a bridge over the Afon Llwyd river in order that some of his parishioners could get to church on Sundays. *Pont* means bridge and the name David ap Howell was to become Pont David ap Howell and shortened to become Pont ap Howell, and indeed if said quickly would sound like Pontypool.

Pontypool and its surrounding districts contained many heavy industries in the form of forges and ironworks that have now disappeared from our landscape, but with the help of maps, photographs and a little research, then we can piece many things together. It is with this in mind that we are attempting to explain where some of these early industries were located, and the manner in which they operated.

It was David and Ieaun Grant who, in 1425, on the banks of the Afon Llwyd river – said to be at Pontymoile – who set up small forges, probably known then as "Bloomeries", and were responsible for some of the first iron-making in Pontypool, but it was the Hanburys who were to greatly enhance any iron industry that may have been on going here with the arrival of "Richard Hanbury, Goldsmith" (Banker) from London in around 1565 to 1570. From that time on perhaps it is fair to say that management – and the industrious people of Pontypool – who worked these forges and mills would for many years to come be the leaders in the world of iron-making. Richard was involved with a firm, "The Society of Mineral and Battery Works", who had set up numerous works in different parts of the country, with one of their enterprises being at Tintern making Osmonde Iron, which was used in the making of wire. At that time wire was in great demand throughout the country, being used mainly in the wool industry for carding (combing wool for the cloth trade). It seems that the Tintern site had already been an ironworks, but had become run down, hence it is said that the Mineral and Battery Company had sent several men to turn the works losses into a profit, but in fact in a short time it seems they had run up debts in excess of £3,000. Richard Hanbury, who had himself acquired a share in the Mineral and Battery Company, found himself at Tintern as the Company's representative, to hopefully put things right. The loss it seems was quickly turned into a profit by the efforts of this far-sighted businessman, but this was only the start of an enterprise of some standing, for it was around this time that Richard and Edmund Wheeler, his now partner, had turned their attention to South Wales, where they had set up several iron making establishments in their own names, among them a forge and furnace between Pontypool and Crumlin, along with several other enterprises, among them establishments at Cwmffrwdoer, and another at Monkswood, with the latter being erected in 1568, and all set up in a short time and all seemingly making a profit. They had come to a part of the world where all the resources necessary for making iron were at their fingertips in great abundance, in the form of ironstone, limestone, timber for making charcoal, and at that time the untapped power of water. With regard to the Tintern works, these Pontypool furnaces and forges could provide the type of iron – Osmonde – needed to make wire products, and indeed from the onset Richard was supplying their needs from here, but then it seems that he and Edmund found that they could do better on their own account, and eventually this situation was to cause many disagreements with other shareholders at the Tintern works.

Remains of the furnace

Remains of a furnace at Tintern

This photograph shows the remains of a single furnace located in the Angidy Valley at Tintern, and was operated for the purpose of producing iron. Probably a similar furnace to this one, along with a wire works, was also located in this area and in operation by the Society of Mineral and Battery Works in around 1560–1570. The water for the over-shot water wheel on this site was stored in holding ponds (still visible), and was conveyed to the wheel in a sluice mounted on the stone pillars, seen top right of this photograph. The water for the ponds was fed from the Angidy, a tributary to the Wye, which at one time had numerous water wheels creating power for industry along its route. In 1979 – 1981, this site was excavated, and with the use of interpretation boards, explain just how the works operated. Conjectural drawings give an idea of what the buildings that were once on site were used for. One building contained the products needed to make iron, while another information board explains that Iron ore used here at one stage came from the Forest of Dean, but later it was found that it was more economical to ship iron ore in from Cumberland, which was a journey of 250 miles. As seen in this next photograph there is a row of cottages (Furnace Cottages) now owned by Mr. And Mrs Saunders overlooking the site, and indeed these cottages once housed some of the furnace workers. It is not known whether these cottages would have been rebuilt at some time.

Tintern

This recent photograph shows the same site at Tintern, now sadly overgrown and waterlogged. The photograph below is of an information board on the same site, it shows in the centre the building for storing iron making materials, while on the right of the picture can be seen the race or "launder" carrying the water to the over shot water wheel.

The name Tintern is significant: "Terne" Plate is iron plate coated with a mixture of lead and tin, the reason being, lead will not adhere to iron but tin will. Such a coating was necessary to help prevent corrosion, such as rusting.

The power of water was paramount for the industries and they had been strategically placed alongside the rivers where there was an ample water supply. Starting near Pontnewynydd, and working down river, a system of leats and weirs was put in place to raise the water level to a point where the water could be diverted from the river into holding ponds. This water was then used mainly to drive waterwheels which in turn operated iron-making equipment. In order to understand where some of these forges and mills in and around Pontypool were located, we will view a sketch from the late 18th century.

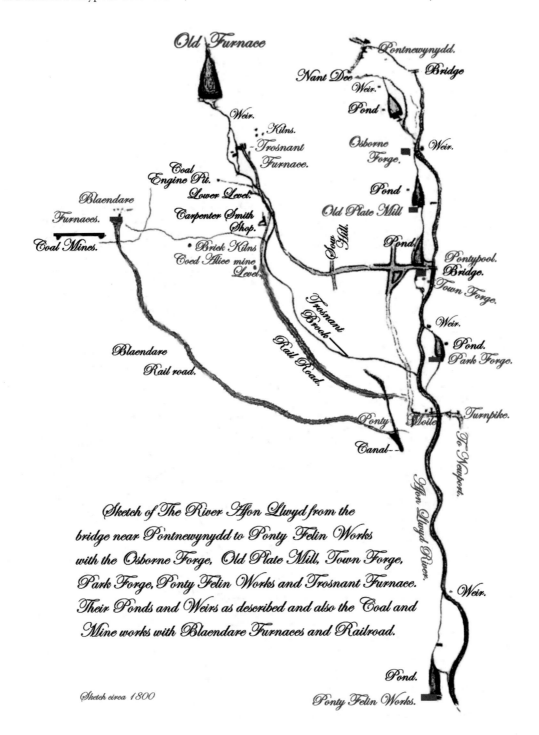

Sketch of The River Afon Llwyd from the bridge near Pontnewynydd to Ponty Felin Works with the Osborne Forge, Old Plate Mill, Town Forge, Park Forge, Ponty Felin Works and Trosnant Furnace. Their Ponds and Weirs as described and also the Coal and Mine works with Blaendare Furnaces and Railroad.

Sketch circa 1800

Moving down the Afon Llwyd river from the bridge at Pontnewynydd, which would be the bridge at the junction of Hospital Road and Mill Road, we can see the locations of the holding ponds and the forges and mills en route.

The first forge we come to is the Osborne which had probably been established in excess of 400 years ago, and was on the site of the present Nant Ddu (black brook) day centre, and where a weir can still be seen nearby. The old plating mill would have stood on what is now the Riverside multi-storey car park, while the Town Forge, before it was moved in 1831 was reputed to have been within twenty yards of the Cross, which is considered to be the centre of Pontypool.

The Park Forge, as its name indicates, was located in Pontypool Park on or near the site of the present day leisure centre. This forge was also dismantled in 1831, but not rebuilt as was the Town Forge.

The last local forge shown on our sketch was the Pontyfelin works, which had been established at Lower New Inn between 1703 and 1720, but was dismantled by the turn of the century. According to the information appended by this sketch, by 7 February 1800, this works was in perfect working order, being well stocked and manned.

In order to provide iron in significant amounts for these forges and mills, then the iron ore had firstly to be mined and processed in great furnaces. One such furnace, probably the first in the vicinity, was built by Richard Hanbury and his partner Edmund Wheeler in around 1565. If we follow our sketch from the Afon Llwyd river near Pontymoile by way of the Trosnant Brook, we will find the location of that furnace and holding ponds (Glyn Ponds) that were located in the village of Old Furnace, between Pontypool and Crumlin on the A472.

The Glyn Ponds, known locally as the "Fish Ponds", were put in place to feed the needs of the furnaces, but sadly, both ponds were filled in with colliery waste between the mid-1950s and the mid-1970s from the new mine at Hafodyrynys, along with a large part of the side of the valley. This new mine received the colliery waste from several collieries all linked underground by the new mine, which included Tirpentwys and Blaenserchan.

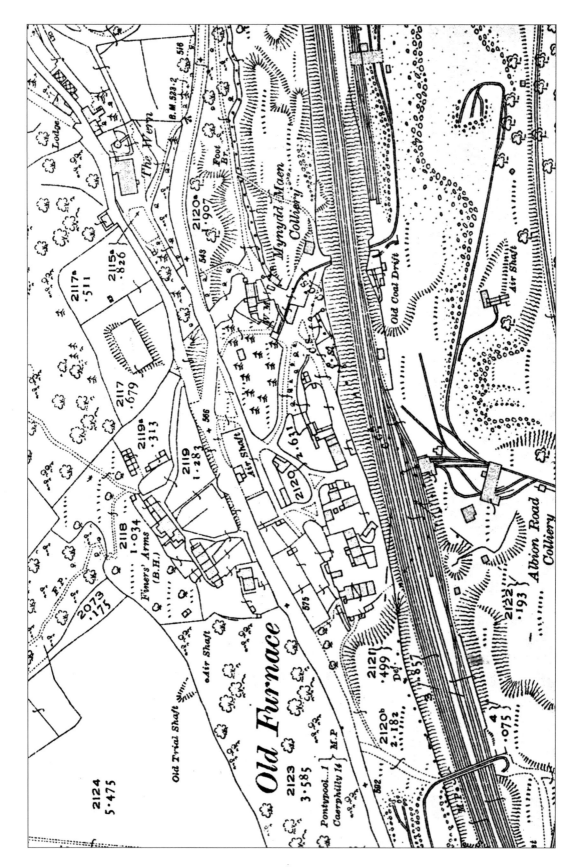

Capel Hanbury Leigh 1776–1861

In 1803 Capel Hanbury Leigh was to enter into an agreement which allowed the Monmouthshire Canal company to enlarge the existing dams to collect more water, in order that they could take any excess to top up their canal. These dams were later breached with the coming of the railway in the mid-1800s, as can be seen in the photograph below.

Photograph courtesy of Sir Richard Hanbury Tenison KCVO

This railway, the Newport, Abergavenny and Hereford Railway Company's Taff Vale Extension, led on to yet another great engineering feat, the Crumlin Viaduct, the iron for which was rolled in Blaenavon.

The Crumlin Viaduct was started in 1853, and was a remarkable piece of engineering by any standards. It was just over two hundred feet high and fifteen hundred feet long, or, if one includes the stone abutments, one thousand six hundred and fifty-eight feet long. The piers were made up of fourteen hollow cast-iron columns, the longest being one hundred and seventy feet long, and twelve inches in diameter; these columns were made up of ten lengths, each seventeen feet long, with the width at the top, between the hand-rails, being twenty-six feet. All the castings were made at Falkirk, Scotland, by the firm of Kennard. One pier was built in the centre of the canal, and was known as "The Lady Isabella" after Lady Isabella Fitzmaurice, who opened the Viaduct. Beneath this pier was buried a cup containing coins of the period – that was on 8 December 1853.

Tragedy at the Upper Glyn Pond

It was on this pond in 1868 that a multiple drowning took place. On Thursday 23 July 1868 a boat carrying a number of people was holed by debris in the bottom of the pond, allowing water to rush in.

The outcome of this resulted in the tragic loss of nine lives.

The dead were:

Campbell, aged 16 years, Kate aged 15 years, Jessie aged 14 years, and Granville aged 11 years, the children of E.B. Edwards, Esq. Solicitor and Clerk to the magistrates for this division, Glanwern House, Pontypool.

Eleanor aged 34 years, eldest daughter of James Essex, Esq, surgeon, Pontypool.

Emma Maud, aged 17 years, daughter of the Revd Dr James, Rector of Panteg, near Pontypool.

Frances, aged 23 years, daughter of Mr William Ion, Abersychan.

Janet Mary, aged 13 years, only daughter of Dr R. Sloper of the Aberdare Iron Works.

Luke Sanger, aged 53 years, servant, of the boathouse, Upper Glyn Pond.

Chapter 2. Old Furnace

Iron was being produced at the Old Furnace as far back as 1576, and in fact tradition tells us that in order to prevent iron from being produced here, Oliver Cromwell's troops destroyed the furnace here and much of the iron-making capabilities in 1645, but the furnace and refineries were later restored and in working order once again.

With regard to the reference to refineries above, it is of interest that in the village of Old Furnace, about 100 yards away, there is a house that was once an inn called "The Finers Arms".

The furnace (looking like a large pot) can be seen next to and on the right of the white houses that are on the extreme left of the photograph, and was intact when this photograph was taken around the 1950s, and indeed the furnace was still visible as late as 1979.

As a boy, living in the village and passing the furnace regularly, I (Clive Davies) often wondered what its purpose was. Unfortunately, records for this – the Trosnant site – seem to be very sparse, but I remember that running between the two corrugated roofed buildings near to the furnace was a strong water course, which may have been the source of power for a waterwheel. When the site was excavated in the 1970s, in the foundations of one of the buildings were several large cut stones that may well have been remnants of the original works. Today the area where the furnace stood has been covered in as part of the foundations when the new road from Pontypool to Hafodyrynys was being constructed.

Near the public house – The Finers Arms – ran a tram road; this started at a place called Blaenycwm, near Pant-y-gasseg, some two miles away, passing close to, and possibly serving, the Trosnant furnace which it could have been supplying with materials, and finally terminating at Pontymoile.

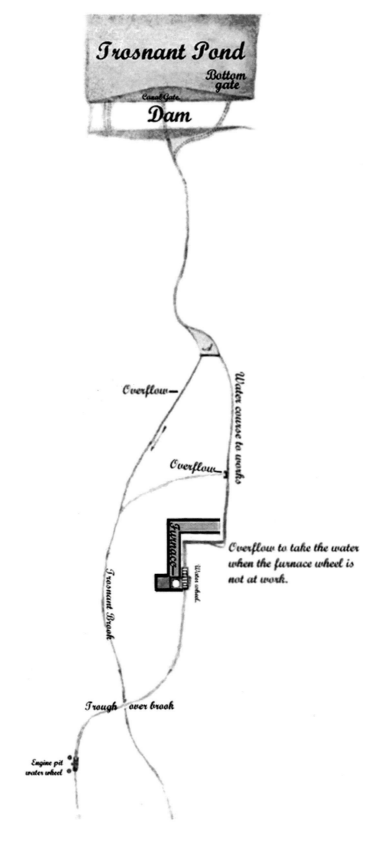

What is interesting from the time of this old sketch is that the pond, like the Trosnant furnace, was once called the Trosnant Pond, while later becoming the Glyn Ponds. It can also be seen that water which was being provided for the Monmouthshire Canal and the furnaces shared the same watercourse, so it seems that the water from the dam, due to it being so valuable, was in some way being regulated. The watercourse for the canal gate was from the centre of the dam and is still in place, as can be seen in this next photograph taken in 2007.

The other outlet from the pond shown on the sketch, extreme right of the dam, was the gate that fed the furnaces, and would have been destroyed by the railway company while laying their tracks in the mid-1800s.

Prior to the time when the ponds were filled in with colliery waste the area was a beautiful place where many people would gather around in order to enjoy boating, swimming and picnics which lasted right into the late evenings. Many of the water channels were full of watercress and also the surrounding edges of the ponds contained many bullrushes that would waver gracefully in a summer's breeze, and most important, the whole area was a haven for wild life.

The sketch shows a similar set up to what would have been in place at that time at the Trosnant Furnace, with a pond similar to that of the Glyn Ponds, providing the water for a waterwheel, which in turn raised and lowered bellows, alternately producing the blast that was needed to raise the temperature in the furnace to the melting point of the iron. The furnace would have been fed like this from the top with ironstone, limestone, and charcoal; these materials would have been stored on the furnace bridge. When the furnace charge was molten, the impurities (slag) floated on top of the heavier iron; the slag was then removed (tapped off) by way of a hole in the furnace wall called a slag notch. Since the slag was floating on the iron the slag notch would have been positioned above the iron tap hole.

The iron was then released (tapped) into sand moulds, and because of the way the moulds were set out, lying end-on to the metal runner, which was called a "sow", were said to resemble piglets feeding from a sow; from this came the name for the cast iron being produced as pig iron, which the workmen referred to, naturally enough, as pigs.

The photograph shows lengths of pig iron, which came in varying lengths, usually around 3 feet, as can be seen by this 2 feet ruler giving scale, and with the weight of each bar being between 70 and 100 lbs.

But since these cast pigs were very brittle, they often broke during handling, or were broken for ease of handling. The fact that the pigs were broken was of little importance since the length did not matter.

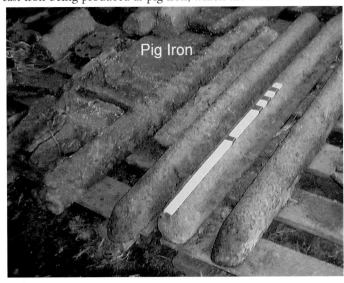

Pig Iron

Chapter 3. Minerals

The pig iron was loaded onto pack mules and horses like these, and then transported via the Tranch to Sow Hill – apparently so called from the sows and pig iron – which was near to the top of High Street, Pontypool, and from where the pig iron was then distributed to the local forges for further processing.

The person in the photograph on the right is holding a large piece of ironstone or iron ore. It was commonly called "kidney ore" from its shape and colour, which was usually in rounded masses (reniform = kidney shaped) and dark red, which when melted in the furnace with the heat from charcoal, formed pig iron. As explained it was also necessary to add limestone, usually about ten per cent of the charge, which acted as flux to form a slag and to help remove impurities. To obtain ironstone in the early stages the ironmakers would look to the surrounding hills where the mineral outcropped in numerous places near the surface.

"Scouring" was one of the first methods of mining, and would have found whole families, including children, on a mountainside. These people loosened the surface soil, grasses, etc. with picks, after which water stored in a pond was released to wash away the loosened surface material, exposing the outcrop mineral seam ready for extraction; this left behind the heavy ironstone to be collected and taken to the furnace. "Outcrop" means the end of a seam of minerals coming out near the surface. In fact, this could be said to be the forerunner of opencast mining.

Wherever this sort of enterprise was going on, other people very often suffered the consequences, which could be serious, such as houses being flooded, or inundated with spoil, such as mud, grasses, stone ,etc, washed down from the workings by the uncontrolled force of water once released from the storage ponds. This was to lead to much litigation involving Mr Hanbury and the unfortunate recipients of this rubbish.

The picture above shows the actual remains of the sluice gate which controlled the water from the pond, situated at Penyrheol, above the Upper Race and Blaendare. At the time when this method of mining was carried out, it was also known as "Hushing" and it also seems likely that in the context of a district, the name of the area, the "Race", came from the water "race" when the water was released from the pond to "scour" the overburden away. (The dictionary definition of "Race" is "A fast flowing channel or the water in it").

This same process of scouring was also used for extracting coal seams, and any coal that would have found itself washed down to the river was collected up by people, who as well as using it for their fires would supplement their own income by selling it to the local inhabitants.

These operations left a scar on the mountainside approximately 500 meters long, 60 meters wide, and up to 10 meters deep, and because of these facts, the area has now been awarded Grade Two listed status.

In 1740, the great John Wesley preached here at the Scourings to a crowd of some 600 people. It is also a fact that the wife of Thomas Allgood, of Japan ware fame, after listening to the great man, herself became a convert.

Iron Ore

Magnetite contains around 72.5% iron, Hematite 70%, and Limonite 60%.

Hematite (Fe_2O_3) when relatively pure contains around 70% iron and 30 % oxygen, and is the most common and important of all the iron ores. Colours vary from dark red to grey or even black, and can be in massive lumps or a coarse powder.

Hematite often occurs in dark red rounded reniform masses, giving it its common name "Kidney Ore".

Magnetite (Fe_3O_4) is the richest – and purest, (containing 72.4% iron) of all iron ores. It is strongly magnetic and is black in colour, and usually free from both sulphur and phosphorus, both very undesirable in iron-making.

Next to aluminium, the most abundant element on earth is iron, making up around 4.5 per cent of the earth's crust.

It rarely occurs in the pure state, and is generally found in the form of oxides, carbonates, sulphides and silicates, with the oxides being by far the most important. Economically, however, the three most important minerals are Magnetite, Hematite and Limonite.

Some varieties of magnetite were highly magnetic and were known as lodestone, which was used in ancient times as a compass for navigation.

Chapter 4. Charcoal

As already explained the fuel used during the 1500s and into the 1800s was charcoal, which meant that in order to operate one of these furnaces one would need colossal amounts of woodland.

Photograph courtesy of the Royal Forest of Dean

Charcoal is the black or brown carbonized residue of partially burned wood. As far as iron-making is concerned, to produce a ton of iron requires roughly five times as much charcoal as coke. In early times charcoal was produced by covering a stack of wood with turf in order to exclude air, but leaving a small cavity, usually at the top, for igniting the stack, which was done by introducing red hot embers, placing a metal lid over the hole, and then allowing it to burn slowly over several days.

Rather than transport the heavy timber to the furnaces and forges, charcoal was produced in the forest It needed 10 tons of timber to produce 2.5 tons of charcoal, which is four times lighter for the mules and packhorses to carry. Charcoal burning was said to be a very skilled process.

The demand for the fuel was so great that prior to coke replacing charcoal many of the furnaces had been closed due to the stripping of local woods and forests. Timber as felled was bought and sold in measured amounts called cords, (a Cord being a pre-metric measurement of 128 cubic feet, or in metric, 3.6 cubic meters).

During the time when so much woodland was being felled for charcoal then it is obvious that disputes would arise between people who needed quality timber, such as builders who were needing good timber to apply their trade and indeed, on several occasions it was becoming so scarce that at one time only two furnaces were working in the whole of Monmouthshire. This situation was to see violence, threatening the Hanburys' wood cutters on several occasions.

Eventually it was found by Abraham Darby of Coalbrookdale through his experiments, that coal when converted to coke could fire furnaces more efficiently, therefore at a lesser cost, which meant that the mid-1700s saw many furnaces changing over to the new fuel.

Coke is the carbonised residue of coal. Carbonisation is accomplished by heating the coal, thus driving off the volatile constituents, such as gases and tar.

The other product now needed was limestone. Today many old limestone quarries can still be seen which produced it, as for example this one at Abersychan.

Limestone is calcium carbonate, which can be as soft as chalk or as hard as marble. When broken up to a suitable size, around two to four inches (usually by young boys and girls), it was then added to the blast furnace charge. The charcoal, ironstone and limestone were laid in the furnace in layers and with the furnace lit and well underway, then more of the products were added to the furnace charge when required.

The optimum size mentioned, i.e. two to four inches, was necessary so that sufficient gaps were left in the charge for the passage of the air blast.

This photograph is of the lime kilns at Abersychan

It was connected to the quarry in the previous photograph by a small inclined way: the limestone was brought down this same inclined way, some of which was crushed for road metal, building etc., while a large amount was fed into the top of the kilns, of which there were four.

The photograph below shows one of four kilns which has been partly filled in.

The limestone was mixed with coke in these kilns and was burned, the length of time taken to burn depending on the hardness of the limestone, i.e. the harder the stone the longer it took to burn. Heating the limestone in this way decomposed it, driving off the carbon as carbon dioxide which then escaped through the top of the kiln, leaving the calcium behind in the form of quicklime, some of which was used by mixing it with boiler ashes and water to form black mortar, which could be described as an early form of cement. It supplied many of the local building firms. The mortar mill was located just inside the entrance gate on the left-hand side.

The reader will notice that this process is almost identical to that which happens in a blast furnace: but here the end product is lime rather than iron.

Outlet

Outlet

Outlet

Outlet

This photograph shows the four lime outlets at the bottom of the four kilns.

This is where the quicklime was extracted after burning; the lime produced here, as well as being used for mortar, had other uses too such as a soil improver for treating acid soil, also for white liming – and waterproofing – the exterior of buildings.

Limestone

Limestone is a sedimentary rock which consists of more than 50% by weight of calcium carbonate. It may be organic, formed from the calcareous skeletal remains of living organisms; chemically precipitated; or detrital, formed from the remains of pre-existing limestones, but the majority are organic, and were, so we are told, usually deposited in shallow water, like the corals of tropical waters.

Put very simply, limestone is necessary in iron-making for the formation of a slag; it combines with the oxidised impurities, such as silicon, manganese, iron oxide, and phosphorus, to form a fusible slag. A reasonably pure limestone is required, which contains a minimum of acid constituents.

The physical size of the limestone is important; it should be in lumps varying from about four to six inches in size, with a minimum of small pieces and dust, which would block the furnace airflow.

The quantity used varies between five and ten per cent of the furnace charge, and is usually kept in proportion to the amounts of silicon, Phosphorus, etc. in the metal.

Raw materials used in recent years are, to make a ton of iron, roughly: iron ore (metal content about 50%) two tons: Coke, 0.9 of a ton, limestone; about 0.5 of a ton, plus 4 TONS of air!

But in the early days of iron-making, these quantities would have been very different. For example, instead of two tons of coke to make a ton of iron, many times that amount of charcoal would have been needed, due to its lower calorific value; this led, inevitably, to the denuding of local woodlands.

Chapter 5. American's Visit

At this time we would like to mention a visit around the British Isles by an American, James Ramsey Patterson, who as part of his visit was on a fact-finding mission to obtain information on the process of tin plate manufacture mainly around Pontypool. So while taking a look at these industries we will also be aware of the American's journal. He arrived here at the Trosnant furnace on 7 January 1828, and in his own words said that: "It is a single furnace – blown – by a water wheel about 30 feet high, 3 feet wide and 12in deep in the shrouding – an over shot wheel. – they use coke – one carbonating furnace with two blasts – they have here coal mines and a larger place in the form of ovens for making coal & coking thru' coal."

(Thru coal, or properly "Through" is a mixture of lump and small coal.)

It would also appear from the American's words that they were indeed using coke here in the latter days of iron-making at the Trosnant Furnace; if that be the case, then mines would by now have been opened.

One method of mining for coal in early times was by the use of bell pits. Bell pits were among the earliest methods of mining and were sunk to allow the miners to go below ground to mine the seams near the surface. The coal was then dug out in a "Bell" shaped hole, and with the use of a windlass the coal was wound to the surface. This was done until the surrounding ground became undermined, making it too dangerous to work further, or when the miners judged it too dangerous to work further. That bell pit was then abandoned and another opened nearby. It was said that the new pit would be opened at a distance at which a man could throw a shovel of earth from the original pit, so the process would start again and so on.

Another method of raising coal or minerals from a mine was by a gin. This was a round barrel-type structure, on which was wound a rope or chain. It was mounted vertically in two bearings and attached to it was a projecting arm, which in turn was attached to a horse's harness. As the horse walked in a circle, so the rope or chain wound around the drum, hoisting the bucket or skip from the mine.

Levels or drift mines tunnels were driven into the hillsides in order to reach the seams or veins of coal.

The last two horses to work in a British coal mine were at Pant-y-gasseg near Pontypool and were named Gremlin and Robbie (pictured previous page). Both were retired in 1999, with Gremlin going to Milton Keynes RSPCA, the home for retired pit ponies, while Robbie went to an English mining museum.

Gremlin can be seen having worked his last shift and pulled his last tram of coal. Mike Desmond is leading him out from the mine for the last time. Mike's family have been involved with small mines for over 70 years, and he said that it bought a tear to his eye seeing both horses going. These feelings are reflected in Mike's body language.

Note the horse's protective headwear (above). This protected his face and eyes against injury from bumping against the tunnel timbers and from falling stones, etc. An average early type tram of dry coal would probably weigh around fourteen or fifteen hundredweight (700–750kg).

Photographs supplied by Martin.Ellard@Dragon-pictures.com

Osborne Forge

The Osborne forge (Little Forge), with Mill House – a watermill – on the right of the picture, could very well have been erected here more than 400 years ago, being located on the site of the present-day Nant Ddu (black brook) day centre, which is within one hundred yards or so of the bottom of Merchant's Hill at Pontnewynydd. The forge produced Osmonde iron mainly in bar form for wire-making, with the iron said to be most malleable and ductile; it indeed was famous in the reign of Elizabeth I and James I, and due to its high quality was the only iron to be used by their governments. Much of the iron was drawn into wire to be used in wool carding – a type of combing for the wool trade.

History tells us that the name Osborne was originally called "Asleom", a name which was changed to Osmond by an act of Charles I. This was eventually corrupted to Osborne, after which Osborne Road, previously Manchester Road, was named.

Toward the end of the 1600s Major John Hanbury, with his employee Thomas Cook, experimented with different ways of making iron plate, which at the time was being used for the making of kitchen utensils such as kettles, pots, pans, etc. This way of producing plate was by the use of the hammer, but these two men were about to create a piece of industrial history, by inventing the first method of *rolling* iron plates as opposed to hammering.

This was probably done by modifying rolls which may have been used for rolling narrow strips of iron. Red hot iron bars measuring two feet long by four inches wide were fed through the modified rollers, with each bar being rolled from four inches wide to several feet.

A drawing of what the first rolling mill in Pontypool would have looked like

The rollers are in the centre, held down with bolts and cross bars. The two thick cylinders left and right of the image are the shafts of the two waterwheels that were needed to drive the mill. This configuration required that the waterwheels had to run in opposite directions. This in turn meant that one wheel needed to be what is called a "Pitch-Backshot", which simply means that the flow of the water feeding the wheel is reversed at the top of the wheel, so that the one wheel rotates the opposite way to the other, and indeed, we know that there were two water wheels at the Osborne Forge, which gives credence to the previous drawing.

This process produced flat iron plate much quicker, at the same time being much more cost effective, while also giving a much more uniform finish. So successful was their invention that they were soon outdoing their competitors, and indeed it left Major John Hanbury's works hard pressed to manufacture sufficient plate to supply their customers, both in the United Kingdom and abroad.

We know that there was a plating mill near the Old Estate Yard at Pontymoile close to the canal junction, but probably the extent of the output of the new invention – the rolling mill – exceeded their expectations, and this would have necessitated larger works for rolling iron plate, one of which would probably have also been called the plating mill, or as we now know it, "The Old Plating Mill", which was located on the site of the present day's multi storey car park on the Riverside estate, and would have incorporated the newly invented rolling mill.

It seems highly probable that this same man, Major John Hanbury, was also responsible for importing the art of making tin plate into Pontypool, and thereafter the whole of Britain; but the authors – despite much research – have been unable to obtain a definitive date for this enterprise, because there are a number of dates given by different authorities, which vary between 1703 and 1743.

From an entry in the Royal National Eisteddfod, Cardiff, dated 1883, "Transactions", and published by Duncan and Sons, Cardiff , we find the following:

"It is generally believed that the tin-plate works of Pontypool were erected about the year 1720, and this belief is even shared by the most reliable authorities upon the subject, as will appear from the following quotations: Doctor Ure, in his Dictionary, writes – 'About the year 1720, a works for the manufacture of tin-plates were established at Pontypool, and this seems to be the earliest of such works in England that was permanently successful.' In the 'Penny Encyclopaedia' we find that a Mr Parkes, who read a paper 'Tinning,' before the Philosophical Society at Manchester in 1818, declared that 'The tin manufacture was first introduced into this country at Pontypool, between the years 1720 and 1730.' Archdeacon Coxe also agrees in assigning the invention to the year 1720. But it is well to remark that the Pontypool Iron and Tin-plate Company date the establishment of their business from the year 1703. It would certainly be presumptuous on our part to try and disprove, without strong evidence, the statements of the noted writers to whom we have referred, and equally presumptuous would it be of the Company which we just mentioned to date the commencement of their concern without full and reliable testimony. In this instance, however, we are dealing with facts, and we reckon then we have been particularly fortunate in having had access to means which will enable us to arrive at the truth of the question. The following letter, which is addressed by the present agent of the Hanbury Estate to Mr Josiah Richards, the senior partner of the present Pontypool Iron and Tin-plate Company, we hope will prove, not withstanding the united testimony of high authorities, that the popular belief on this subject is wrong:

"Copy Park Estate Office Pontypool, Monmouthshire, June 23-1874.
"Dear Sir, The price which Mr Hanbury obtained for his "Pontypool Plate" in 1704 was:

"Singles," £26 10s per ton.
"Doubles," £28 10s per ton.
These delivered to Gloucester or Bristol.
In London : £33 "Singles"
£35 "Doubles"
The thinnest doubles at £37, and the very thickest singles £37 0s, 0d.

"To J. Richards, Esq. I am sir Yours Truly Signed A. A. Williams."

Sir Richard Hanbury Tenison tells us in his book *The Hanbury's of Monmouthshire*, that the Pontyfelin mill may have been the first to produce tin plate in Britain, although Sir Richard also states that there was a mill near the Old Estate Yard, which may also lay claim to the same title.

A major difficulty in the early days of tin plate manufacture was cleaning the plates for tinning. Anyone who has used a soldering iron will be aware of the need for absolute cleanliness of the metal. This was accomplished in the early days by scrubbing with sand and water, this method being eventually superseded by immersing the sheets for a period of time in the fermented lees of bran (fermenting the lees made them acid, which was sufficiently strong to remove scale and dirt from the sheets) after which the edges were filed smooth, and the sheets covered in resin – the resin acting as a flux – prior to being hand-dipped in a container of molten tin, called in those days "Cambrian Silver". Using this method, they were unable to control the thickness of the coating of tin, so that this method was very wasteful. This problem was overcome when the tin pot was invented about the year 1745.

Marking with the works stamp and packing then followed. It was around 1760 that the sheets were first cleansed in diluted hydrochloric acid before being annealed, after which they were placed in bran lees for some time then finally cleaned with diluted sulphuric acid.

Japan Ware

Japan ware was introduced into Pontypool around 1660 by Mr Thomas Allgood, who was a native of North-ampton, and it was through his talent and later that of his family, in the art of japanning, that their names will always be associated with the art of Pontypool Japan ware, for even today, the product is still very desirable and certainly highly collectable. Japanning was a form of high-quality lacquer work that originated in China in the 6th century, and soon after was copied by the Japanese. Many items were created using the lacquered designs including candlesticks, trays, tea urns and snuff boxes, etc.

It was at the Osborne Forge that the iron used in the manufacture of the famous Japan ware was pro-duced, firstly by the use of the hammer, and later by the plates being rolled through rolling mills. The important job of cleaning the plates was usually left to women and children, and was accomplished by scrubbing with water and sand, but as already explained this method was later superseded by immersing the plates in lees of fermenting bran. The plates were then taken a little way down river to the Plating Mill where they were worked by people called "Press Stampers", who were responsible for stamping the plates to the shape of the articles required. In some cases it seems that a sheet of plate was placed over a die of the shape required, and the opposite die, which was suspended by a crane, was allowed to drop in order to produce the required shape (this process would be called "Drop-forging" today). From the plating mill the various shaped plates and articles were then transported to the Japan House, which was located at West Place on Crane Street, and it was here that the staff, who were highly skilled individuals, who had come mainly from Birmingham, would use their skills to make and to paint in vivid colours, using, it seems, their own secret enamel made from coal. Once lacquered, the articles were ready for the final process of firing to a saleable finish.

This is Crane Street, Pontypool before the road and town improvements were started around 1990, and just before demolition took place here, but this is one of two entrances into West Place and to their workshops, which would have been used by the Allgood family and their workers. During a breakaway around 1761, several of the family and staff had moved and set up premises at Usk and due to the Usk Japanners painting butterflies on many of their products, it is interesting that the Pontypool staff, who considered the Usk ware to be imitation, had nicknamed the Usk staff the "Butterflies"!

It is also very likely that the house in the background of this photograph would have been as old as the one they had worked in. The secret of Japan ware was exactly that, for no one, apart from the workers, was allowed anywhere near to where the process was taking place. Even those of the family that had moved to Usk had kept the process secret, and what a secret, for it was to last for as long as the process continued, which was until 1860 when the last pieces were produced.

The Pontypool Japan ware seems to have been superior to other types of Japan ware, and the following amusing story was taken from a book which relates to Pontypool local register (appendix page 5 and 6) that states: "That its superiority was demonstrated by 'Old Billy Allgood', as he was familiarly called by his friends: Being one evening at his neighbours, the 'Red Lion', a Birmingham traveller in the same line being present among the company in the bar, the conversation turned upon the Japan trade, and the traveller asserted that he could produce an article superior to those of Allgood. A wager of five pounds was offered and accepted. Upon the traveller's next journey each was to produce a snuff box, and the persons then present agreed to sit as assessors. At the appointed time the boxes were produced and submitted for inspection by the judges. The finish of each article was equally good; but in design the Birmingham box was declared the best, when up starts Old Billy shouting out: 'Now for the test', calling to the landlord to bring the kitchen tongs. He privately desired the landlord to have a good clear red fire ready. The tongs were brought, when the traveller wonderingly enquired what he wanted with them, 'Why, to put the boxes in the fire, to be sure' replied Billy, 'If that is it' said the traveller, 'I do not guarantee my box to stand fire'"Now," said old Billy in the highest glee, 'now you shall see what real Pontypool Japan is.' He held the box in the fire for a while, and after cooling laid it on the table uninjured, thereby proving (by the old ordeal of fire) the superiority of 'Pontypool Japan'."

Specimens of the Japan ware articles manufactured at Pontypool, which the writer has seen, appear almost as glossy now as ever – a fact which proves the great durability and hardness of the varnish. The process of japanning was always kept a close secret by the Allgood family, and indeed when most of them had died, it seems a pity that the secret had passed on with them.

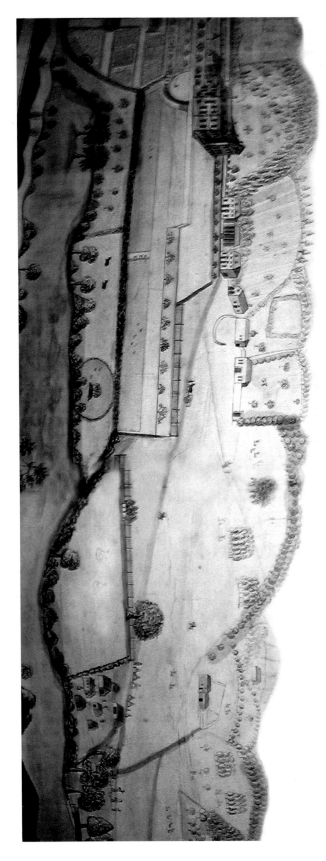

Pontypool Park

The Park Forge

This is part of a drawing of Pontypool Park (shown on previous page), and as far as the as the authors' knowledge extends, it is the only image we have of the location of the Park Forge, and which is reproduced here by kind permission of Sir Richard Hanbury Tenison KCVO, who informed us that the image was almost certainly drawn by one Meredith James of Brecon in 1753. The forge was located bottom right of the drawing, and would have been approximately on the site of the present-day leisure centre, and not far from the home of the Hanbury family, Park House, top left of drawing. Park Forge was initially established to turn pig iron into wrought iron but was later equipped to improve the output.

January the 10th 1828 was to see the American visitor at the Park forge, where, in his own words:

"They were altering and substituting iron for wood. The anvil block is of iron and weighs 6 tons 3 hundred weight. The arms and shrouding of the water wheel which is to work the hammer weighs one side of the wheel 3 tons. The hammer water wheel is about 12 feet diameter and has 22 buckets on it. The shrouders and arms are about 3 inches thick and about 12 inches broad".

(The authors would like to point out that this description given by the American is in his own words. When the American speaks of "Shrouders", he means "Rim Boards": this means the sides of the wheel are raised up each side of the buckets, preventing the loss of water from the sides of the buckets.)

If one walks along the western bank of the Afon Llwyd just south of the leisure centre car park, then one is able to see emerging from the opposite river bank three tunnels (previous page), which are, in the opinion of the authors, the only visible remains of the Park Forge. The right-hand tunnel carries the Nant-y-Gollen stream from the present day Park Lakes, while the centre tunnel would, in the opinion of the authors, have carried the tail race from the forge waterwheel. The smallest of the three tunnels was probably also part of the works, but what its use was must be a matter of conjecture. The authors have mentioned waterwheels, watercourses and holding ponds, etc. frequently. The reader should bear in mind that water power preceded the days of steam, when water – or more often the lack of it! – dictated the output of many ironworks.

This weir and sluice gates are situated just to the north of the Pontypool Leisure Centre car park. Notice also that it is not a single sluice gate; there are two separate gates individually rack and pinion controlled, which we have marked 1 and 2 in the photograph on page 34, and the two control racks are also still in position (which when complete, would have engaged with a cog wheel on a shaft, to which was fitted a handle), as is a small part of the watercourse, or "Leat". At this point the authors would like to put forward a theory as to the use of these sluice gates which almost certainly served the Pontymoile tin works, and perhaps at a later date, Lower Mills (near to the canal junction). The sluice gate marked 3 controlled the water level behind the weir. It can be seen that the stonework of the weir is missing, but when intact, it would have maintained the water level at the top of the sluice gates, and would have extended the full width of the river. The sole idea of this weir is to raise the water level of the river to a sufficient height that it could be diverted to wherever it was needed, i.e. water wheels or holding ponds, and which from its position would most probably have included the holding pond for the Park Forge.

In order to work pig iron into bars the refining was done with the use of a large fired chafery – a type of furnace in which bars of iron are heated – after which the iron was passed under the hammer. This process removed more impurities, thus improving the quality of the metal, after which the metal was suitable for use in the making of plates and rails etc. Later, in 1783 to 1784, this method was to be overtaken when one Henry Cort invented the puddling furnace.

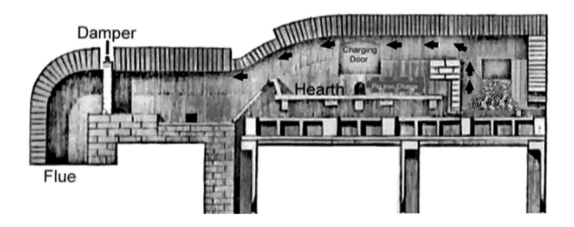

From this side view of a puddling furnace (properly, a reverberatory furnace), it can be seen that a fire is directed over a firebrick wall; the reason for the wall is that the smoke, which contains elements injurious to the iron, such as carbon and sulphur etc., does not come into contact with, and contaminate, the iron. "Puddling" is a term used in iron-making. Put briefly, pig iron is charged to a puddling furnace and heat is applied. After an hour or so, the charge becomes molten; this is assisted by the puddling furnace-man "Rabbling" or stirring the charge. Iron oxide – mill scale – is then added, and the charge is vigorously stirred.

The elements silicon, phosphorus and manganese become oxidised by the mill scale, combining with the iron oxide to form a slag. Carbon is also oxidised into carbon monoxide, causing the molten metal to boil; and as these elements are removed, the melting point rises and the iron becomes a pasty mass. This was known as "Coming to Nature".

The Park Forge, having been one of the first forges to have been established, was about to play a far larger part in iron-working in Pontypool, due to Mr Hanbury making use of the inventions of the said Henry Cort, particularly that of the puddling furnaces, which he – Mr Hanbury – had now installed there. At the same time, modifications were made to the Old Town Forge in the form of rolls for the rolling of iron.

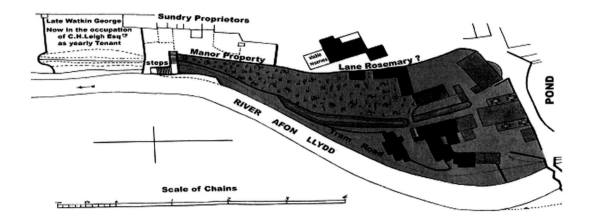

Despite much research, the authors have been unable to date the establishment of the Old Town Forge, but it could very well have been built around the 1560s to 1570s in the time of Richard Hanbury. Its main function seems to have been for converting pig iron into wrought iron, and it appears that in later years, a rolling mill was installed, and if the reader looks on the right of the drawing, he will see what appears to be a depiction of a rolling mill, similar to the one in this drawing

Drawing courtesy of The Newcomen Society

A study of the drawing on the previous page will reveal one man – centre left – dragging a bar from the bar heating furnaces, left, to the roller – centre, while a third man – top left – appears to be reaching into the furnace with tongs for another bar. Note also the waterwheel on the right of the drawing.

The Old Town Forge was situated to the right of the road leading to the park, on Park Road, and behind and on the site of the present-day row of shops on the Town Bridge. This situation obtained until around 1831, when both these forges were dismantled, with the now New Town Forge (New Forge) already having been rebuilt some time earlier further up the river and on the site of the Old Plating Mill, and the Park Forge dismantled completely, as because of their proximity to Park House, the home of the Hanbury family, the noise from the increasing use of machinery was becoming intolerable. For instance, now that the power of steam had arrived then probably a steam hammer may have been used that would have looked similar, but much smaller than, this steam hammer photographed at Blaenavon 2005.

Starting at the top, we have: the steam cylinder, and below that the piston rod, below again in the centre is the hammer proper, called "The Tup"

Chapter 6. New Town Forge

This photograph was taken around 1900 after the works had been upgraded in 1871 to produce iron for the tin works but the American visitor was to tell us that when he was visiting the New Town Forge 72 years earlier on 1 January 1828 that:"New years day very wet and rainy and spent morning and greater part of day indoors. During a short cessation of the rain, were up the river and saw the Forge where they make the iron for the tin works. They have five or six establishments, which are all connected by railroads.

"The forge is said to be the most complete in all England *(meaning, we suppose the United Kingdom, Authors)*. The dam, buildings, etc.; are all remarkably neat. The water wheel, Penstock *(Mill Race)* and roof as well, all the supporters, etc: are of iron, handsomely and neatly executed. They run two hammers, one for what they call 'stamping' to which are attached two furnaces, in which they used charcoal to burn the carbonated pigs into nature, and the other is the forge hammer and connected with which are four furnaces, three of which are intended for constant use and one alternately is idle for a week to be repaired; two of them are on one side of the building, and two are on the opposite side. These furnaces are similar to, or are on the principle of, an oven with bottom formed of coke, with blast applied underneath *(the coke bottom)*. The coke bottom burns about twelve inches deep, and to coke applied by a hopper fixed on the back side, and with these, they make 30 tons of iron for the rolling mill of the tin works every week. The forge man told us that the older the pigs, and the older the refined iron were, the better it became and the better it worked for them. They have very large stocks of all on hand. They have water tue-irons."

The American refers to "Tue Irons", properly "Tuyeres", (pronounced "Tweers"), which were originally made of firebrick, and are the nozzles through which air from a large bellows is injected into a blast furnace. In the early days of iron making, these bellows were usually driven by a waterwheel. But in this case the American mentioned "water tue irons", which means they were made of iron and water-cooled.

This may be an appropriate time to temporarily leave the various forges, and pay a visit to the blast furnace (Blaendare) site at the upper race, to investigate operations that had taken place there.

During 1785 the Hanbury family had leased land at Blaendare to one David Tanner from Monmouth, who was responsible for the commencement of several blast furnaces, which he had erected there.

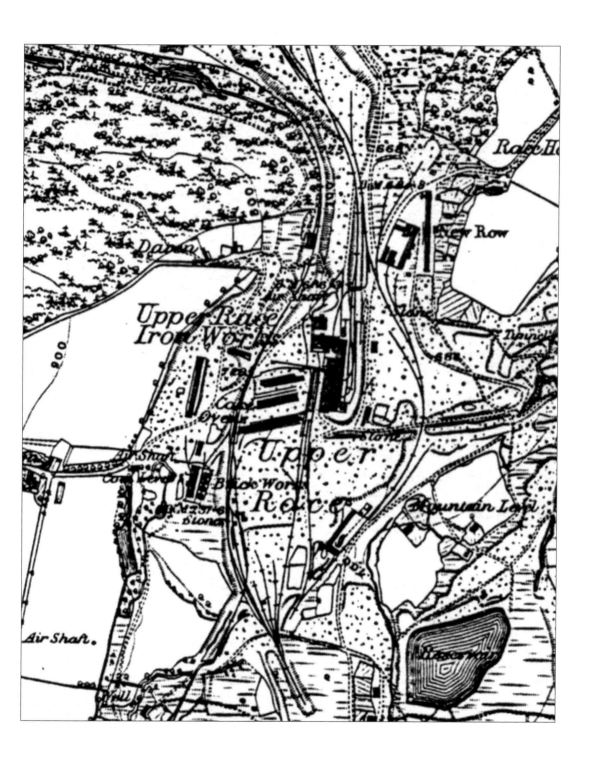

The photograph of Blaendare industrial site with its chimney stacks dominating the skyline, was taken in about 1900 from the top of the Race road where it joins Blaendare Road.

(This is a prime example of the way the land in much of South Wales was being desolated). Just how much time had passed from when the furnaces were demolished, and the time this photograph was taken, is hard to judge.

There had been a huge amount of industry established on this site since well before the 1700s, and indeed the then Capel Hanbury had entered into an agreement with one Edmund Williams to mine coal and operate mine works (*mine* = ironstone) at Cwmlickey in 1684. The industrial site in the photograph had consisted of the ironworks, brickworks, coke ovens and in the near vicinity several collieries large and small could be found producing ironstone, coal and fire clay. In order to obtain the power needed to operate bellows, leats and watercourses were cut along the mountainsides to direct rainwater into storage ponds like this one at Cwmlickey (above), which in turn produced the blast needed to operate these industries.

Water supplies were also going to be needed especially now that steam power in the form of newly invented steam engines was about to come to this area. The Cwmlickey pond is located on the hillside above Blaendare.

The American visitor arrived here (Blaendare) on 9 January 1828, saying: "It is a fine frosty morning visiting these two very large furnaces where they do all their own casting except the chilled rolls *(rolls with a hardened surface)* which are cast at Bristol. They have also two very large air furnaces (SIC) – came home to Pontypool *(when residing at Pontymoile)* through a tunnel under the hill for a railroad."

By 1799 David Tanner had become bankrupt and fled the country. During the next few years the works was upgraded by one Watkin George from Dowlais, whom Capel Hanbury had engaged to reconstruct and modernise this works and those of the forges and mills at Pontypool. The next owner of the Blaendare works was a John Barnaby, who came from Herefordshire, and who had purchased the furnaces for £10,000, but by 1804 found that he was more interested in coal production than developing an ironworks, and so conveyed to Capel Hanbury Leigh the furnaces and several workmen's houses in exchange for land beside the Crumlin Road, near the Twmpath.

Maps show us that the tram lines now introduced from the Blaendare furnaces passed down the hillsides, and through Cwmynyscoy. Today we can still see what probably was the exit point of this tunnel, where the tram road would have passed through and formed part of the route to Pontymoile. To endorse this theory for the tunnel we have the fact that the American visitor in 1828 had said that "He had left the furnaces for Pontypool by way of a tunnel for a Railroad".

It is from near this exit of the tunnel that the route, in the photo, is being pointed out from Blaendare via Cwmynyscoy hamlet (just beyond the trees) to Pontymoile by local councillor and historian Neil Waite.

Up to this time the transport for the pig iron produced at Blaendare, like that of the Trosnant furnace, was taken by packhorses via the Tranch and down to Sow Hill near the top of High Street (Albion Road not being constructed until 1820), but with the Monmouthshire Canal Company building a canal from Pontnewynydd to Newport in 1797, then one of their first major loading points for the iron onto barges would have been near the bottom of today's Victoria Road at Pontymoile, near what was then a flight of locks on the canal, as seen below, unearthed in the 1990s and which showed the remains of the canal and the position of the locks. The building was the lock-keeper's cottage. These loading points would have been somewhere to the left of the picture.

Another point of interest is that the iron pillars on which the beautiful park gates at Pontymoile were hung, were designed by Mr Thomas Deakin, a mining engineer of the Varteg. These were cast at Blaendare, as two sets of four cast iron columns set in a square interlinked with grapevines and the columns cast integral with the base. The handsome railings that enclose the park are said to have been made at the Park Forge by either a Mr William Jarratt or Mr Harry Gunter, the estate smith.

Columns for the Pontymoile park gates

Railings surrounding the park that were reputedly made at the Park Forge.

Now that the furnaces and stock were in the hands of Capel Hanbury Leigh, due to Mr Tanner becoming bankrupt, it was deemed necessary at this time to take the opportunity to upgrade the Blaendare furnaces, along with Capel's own works in the heart of Pontypool. This was to be done with Capel engaging the skills of one Watkin George, who had come down from Dowlais to join the firm and to partner Capel in many of his projects. One of their first acts as partners was to dismantle the wire works at Pontymoile in 1807 and to erect a tin plate works in its place. The tin works was erected partly on the site of the petrol station (below) and the remainder on the ground behind and next to the river, while to the left through the gate behind the car in the foreground stood a gasworks, and on the immediate left where Mr Bullen's roofing firm stands was the Pontymoile foundry.

Trams of wire and later tin plate would have crossed the roadway here near the crossing, and as seen in the second small picture made their way down what would have been originally a tram road, to the Monmouthshire Canal for loading on to barges by use of a small crane, which stood near the canal junction.

While here at Pontymoile, we, the authors, have found at the riverside edge of Mr Skinner's garage, the remains of a leat which comes from under the road and from beneath the petrol station.

This find would endorse our theory that the sluice gate upriver, near the leisure centre, would have been the source of the water for the tin works waterwheel. This tin works was located on the site of the petrol station, and the same water could then be used to enhance the water supply to Lower Mill. Behind the garage site is where the Nant Dare Brook terminated, it started above the Cwmlickey pond, and after feeding the pond, made its way down past the location of the furnaces at Blaendare, where it had supplied power for the furnaces, prior to its being diverted some years earlier, by the late Mr Jim Skinner.

In the opinion of the authors, this brook, "The Dare Brook", would have represented a useful supply of water, and would probably have been used to augment water supplies for Lower Mills. However, once steam power replaced water power, the leat would no longer be required, nor would the extra supply from the Dare Brook, which we know from the map was then directed into the river by means of a small aqueduct. The sluice gate being pointed out by Mr Skinner Junior on the next page appears to have been fitted in order to drain the leat, perhaps for maintenance purposes, and was probably installed at the same time as the sluices already mentioned.

Upon getting up in the morning – 8 January 1828 – the American visitor tells us – again in his own words – that he "Found the ground covered to the depth of 6 inches on a level with snow and still snow-ing moderately. After we had had our breakfast put on our coats and took our umbrellas and walked down along the canal to Leigh & George's Rolling mill *(the Lower Mills?)* where they roll the iron from the plates as it is sent them from the forge, and also into tin sheets for the mill as well as the rolling mill above, and also cut in lengths here for both mills. They have four ovens and two reheating furnaces. Can drive 4 separate pair of rollers or have others attached to the end of them. They cut and trim all the tin iron they roll. The water is brought in trunk or pipes under ground and then raised up in the building so as to act on the water wheel."

The following words by the American are also written in a very ambiguous manner, therefore, as there were, at this particular time, so many tin works between Pontnewydd and Ponthir, the authors were unable to distinguish which mill the American was referring to in the following text. As an example:

Edlogan tin plate works at Pontrhydyrun.

Lower Pontnewydd tin plate works, built 1802.

Ponthir tin plate works, established 1747.

Caerleon tin plate works, established prior to 1749.

"From here walked down the canal and crossed down after going some distance to the tin works next below Leigh & Georges and walked into the rolling mill where they have two sets of rollers for making the sheets for the tin – and two ovens for the rolling mill and an oven in another department for scaling the sheets. From here we went into the room where two young women were scouring the sheets in water and red sand and then put them in troughs filled with a preparation made of an acid for the purpose of clearing it entirely of all scale. When and after being cut to the size – it is taken into another room where it is dipped in the tin and finished. They have 6 places for their tin boilers – five only of which they were using and at which there appeared to be two entire sets of hands where they first took the sheets after be-ing cleared of scale &c and finished tinning it. There were then several women who rubbed and cleaned it with bran – to take off all oil and polish and/burnish it – after which it was taken to another room and assorted and boxed – if any imperfections appear in tinning, too much tin on or anything of that sort, it is scraped and returned again to the dippers – and again under goes the whole process anew. We were very much pleased and gratifyed (*sic*) at seeing the process and hope to be able to see it again more fully in some other works.

The snow being so soft, and being obliged in crossing the road from the canal to the tin works – almost a mile in a creek of water – our boots and stockings completely saturated with water, and we were obliged to wend our way back to Pontypool to change them, where we got just before dark after travelling through snow and water for about ten miles.

An interesting article of local information is given in Mr Harold Cookson's book *Rolling Mills*, 1933, in which he tells us:"The first steel sheet in Britain was rolled at Thompson and Hatton's Bradley Tinplate Works in 1876 from a steel bloom made by Mr Isaac Butler at Panteg Steel works." He also states that:"In 1889, Baldwins commenced rolling steel sheets for galvanising at their Lower Mill works, Pontypool. Iron sheets were being rolled prior to 1870, and the works were in existence in 1818, according to an inscription on the keystone of an arch."

We know also that Lower Mill was, in the early days, driven by a waterwheel; this wheel was 20 feet by 10 feet wide, and the water supply for it was probably taken from a weir and sluice gate on the Afon Llwyd river.

Chapter 7. Iron Ore Mine

As already explained, another method of mining for coal or ironstone was by way of levels or drift mines, which consisted of cutting a tunnel into the hillside to where the mineral was located. One such mine is the Twmpath to Pontnewynydd level, which probably – among others – was another provider of ironstone for the Trosnant furnace. The Twmpath entrance to the tunnel has become lost in time, but is thought to be near the bottom of

Twmpath Hill, while the other entrance is here at Pontnewynydd, where it was unearthed with the building of the new Pontypool bypass. In July 2006 several people, including myself, Clive Davies, entered the mine at this point and were immediately met by water at almost waist level for most of the distance we walked, which was around half a mile.

For most of the distance the tunnel was unsupported, being cut out of solid ironstone, and only needed support where the strata were suspect or fractured, at which time the tunnel was reinforced with stone archways like this one. A chalk mark 1765 on this archway supposes the mine to be at least that old, but more probably the mine is a great deal older than this, for in Sir Richard Hanbury Tenison's book *(The Hanburys of Pontypool)* he explains that the extent of the mine had been recently explored and mapped by Mr W.H. Gascoine, and that the mine, which he called the Droideg level, may well have been started in the late 1600s, with a 650-yard tunnel driven from Old Furnace to the Tranch, and it was at a later time that the tunnel was extended to Pontnewynydd. It does seem likely that when this tunnel was extended, it was purposely built and not just for the mining of iron stone, for it is hard to imagine that they would have gone to the expense of reinforcement such as archways, when the use of timber for tunnel supports would have been far less costly. Since we made the observation as to the use of this tunnel we have gained some extracts of information, written in the *Free Press* in 1870 by W. H. Green, a well-known scribe of the time, who said that "people could still remember the pack horses years before on market day, disrupting the town by knocking over stands and people". So if some elderly people in 1870 could remember these happenings, it seems the tunnel may well have been completed and opened some time between the 1820s and the 1830s. Apart from mining ironstone from the tunnel, they were also relieving themselves of this awkward situation of having the packhorses disrupting the shopkeepers and towns folk.

The route for the iron-laden pack mules and horses from Sow Hill before the tunnel was opened was for the Park Forge down through Trosnant at Pontymoile, while for the Old Town Forge it was down Crane Street, and for the Osborne forge it was via George Street and Wainfelin. It has to be remembered that Manchester Road, later to become Osborne Road, had not yet been constructed.

The whole tunnel for the distance we walked was an array of beautiful autumn colours, and was solid ironstone from roof to floor.

Here we can see here how the early miners had used blocks of ironstone to serve the dual purpose of supporting the roof and creating a side wall. It does also seem that there may have been another section of tunnel behind this side wall that was branching off in another direction.

One had to be amazed at what one was looking at with so many beautiful colours glistening from the stalactites and all of the different shadings, truly a sight for anyone to remember!

It can also be seen from the photograph that one of our members is emerging from a passage he had been exploring; also note the water level on clothing belonging to this group member standing on the right.

No one could leave this mine without imagining just how hard it must have been for the miners who were using only primitive tools such as wedges and sledgehammers – and perhaps a little gunpowder! – to cut through such strata. At the same time, and without realising it, they were cutting themselves a place in history, that left this mine as a testament to themselves, and ensured the name of Pontypool would be captured in the annals of its industrial history.

From what we have written up to now, then it is obvious that Pontypool was a leader in iron-making, and had been so for around 200 years or more, but a more productive time was ahead, for the invention of the steam engine was on our doorstep, and everything was about to change dramatically, for by now other men could see the potential for making money as well as iron, and had started to become involved with iron-making by building larger premises. Examples were Dowlais Iron Works, started as the Merthir *(sic)* ironworks in 1759, and eventually was to become the largest ironworks in the world, with no fewer than eighteen blast furnaces. The Blaenavon iron industry, where just five furnaces were being erected in 1787, was also eventually to grow into a large enterprise.

The remains of the five furnaces at Blaenavon can still be seen to this day and form what is part of the World Heritage Site.

Gunpowder

Put simply, gunpowder is a mixture of three ingredients; 75 per cent potassium nitrate (saltpetre), 15 per cent charcoal, and 10 per cent sulphur. Its invention has been attributed to the Chinese, Arabs and others. It was used from the early times of mining to supplement muscle power; however, one of the main drawbacks to its use was the lack of a suitable fuse. Various methods were used, such as touch papers and straws filled with gunpowder; but none was satisfactory until William Bickford invented the safety fuse in 1831.

Safety fuses consist of a train of blackpowder around which are wound several strands of jute fibre. This is then covered with bitumen varnish, and the whole is waterproofed by a covering of gutta-percha (the coagulated latex of a certain tree). Today, plastics are used.

Gunpowder held the field as an explosive until the latter half of the nineteenth century, when advances in chemistry produced other, more powerful, explosives. Even when closely confined, the pressure gunpowder can generate to do work is only of the order of forty tons per square inch or so, with burning times counted in seconds per metre.

Detonating explosives, however, can easily attain pressures in excess of one thousand tons per square inch, and detonating speeds of anything up to nine thousand metres per second, with the shock wave capable of doing considerable damage.

It was a Professor of Chemistry at Turin University, one Sobrero, who invented nitroglycerine in 1846. Nitroglycerine – an oily liquid – was extremely dangerous to use, and after many accidents, was banned in the United Kingdom.

It was finally tamed by the Swedish chemist, Alfred Nobel. He did this by absorbing the liquid nitroglycerine in a type of clayey sand called "Kieselguhr", 70 per cent nitroglycerine to 30 per cent kieselguhr. This was the original Dynamite, seldom made today.

High explosives have to be detonated; they cannot be ignited. For this a detonator – a copper tube containing a very sensitive explosive which passes from burning to detonation rapidly – is used, and again, it was the discoveries of Nobel which brought this about.

Without these discoveries, the quarrying – for road metal, limestone, etc. – and coal industries would not be able to cope with the demand today..

Chapter 8. Pontnewynydd Forge

This photograph of Pontnewynydd Forge was taken from Hospital Road. Pontnewynydd Forge was erected in 1839, and was variously used as a nail factory and a wire works (Henleys) before eventually becoming a sheet and galvanising works.

Pontnewynydd Steel Works

Pontnewynydd works was registered in 1895, with a capital of £20,000. At that time, it had sixteen sheet mills and eight galvanising pots, with a weekly capacity of some 1,600 tons. But in the late forties it had just twelve mills, six to each engine.

In the picture shown, a smaller mill can be seen this side of the near mill. This was apparently fitted as a temporary arrangement for rolling tin plate when the engine at Town Forge was out of service.

The rolls can be seen in their operating position; and the sheets would have been fed into the rolls from the righthand side of the picture by the roller, who was in charge of the mill.

The two small wheels in front of the mill prevented the hot sheet dragging on the floor while being fed into the rolls. They also assisted the roller when receiving the returned sheet over the top roll from the "Catcher' or, in local parlance, the "Heaver-over". Lubrication of the rolls was accomplished by placing a block of pitch on the "Neck" of the roll; the heat from the roll was sufficient to soften the pitch, allowing it to flow into the roll bearing.

The "Pack Mill" system of rolling started with a pair of hot bars; these were brought to the mill by a boy called the "Bar-dragger" from the coal fired furnaces, just off to the right of the picture. These were then inserted into the mill by the Roller, who rolled them to the required thickness, then one sheet was laid on the other and then they were rolled together, they were then "Doubled", with two of the mill hands taking hold of one end of the "Pack" with a long pair of tongs and folding it over, after which they inserted the bend under the "Doubler", which squeezed the doubled sheets to a sharp bend. The "Pack" was then returned to the furnace for reheating before the next rolling.

After passing through the mill, the sheets were returned to the Roller by the "Catcher" on the opposite side of the mill. He would take the end of the sheet emerging from the mill – again with tongs –and push it back over the top roll. This was also known as "Heaving Over" locally, and was, as were most jobs on a steel mill, extremely hard – and hot – work, especially in summer temperatures; it should be remembered that these sheets were six or seven feet in length and extremely hot.

This procedure was carried out several times, producing eight sheets from a single pair of bars. This procedure gave rise to the term "Pack System" in the sheet industry. This in turn gave way to the more efficient strip rolling mills.

The thickness of the plate being rolled was controlled by the large screw (previous page) on top of the mill standards. In the early days of ironworking, this duty was performed by wedges holding the rolls down; but in many respects, mills would have looked very similar then.

The rolls themselves were of grey cast iron, with a hard "Chill cast" surface.

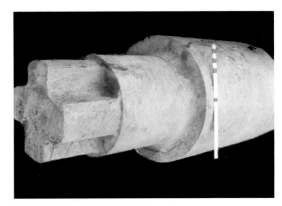

This was one of a pair; the drive from the engine to the rolls was by way of the cruciform end as seen here, which was, in effect, a very coarse spline. The "Neck" or bearing surface of the roll is the smaller diameter next to the cruciform end. Drive to each mill was continuous through the bottom roll in each of the six mills, with each bottom roll in each mill being connected to the next by long spindles.

The roll was cast in a water-cooled iron mould, which caused rapid cooling; this leaves the surface metal white and extremely hard, while at the same time leaving the interior of the roll grey and soft.

The mill engines – "Tandem Compounds" were built by Hick, Hargreaves of Bolton in 1910. Each engine was rated at 1,500 horsepower at 32 rpm.

The cylinder sizes were: Low pressure 65 inches, High pressure 35 inches, six feet stroke. Boiler working pressure was 150 pounds – there were 10 boilers at the works. There was just a single eccentric, since the engines were not reversible.

On the left of the flywheel (below) a ladder can be seen against one of the latticework girders, on which is mounted an electric motor. This motor drove both the Crocodile shears and also the "Doubler" for folding the sheets during rolling.

The photograph on the right shows a pair of crocodile shears, in this case with

both steel cutting edges missing. These were driven from a shaft underneath the steel floor, which was in turn belt driven from an electric motor mounted on one of the girders. Their purpose was to shear the irregular edges from the sheets while at the same time cutting them to size.

The Galvanising process

Galvanising simply meant coating the sheets with zinc metal for protection. This was accomplished by feeding the cleaned sheets through a bath of molten zinc, on which floated a layer of flux.

The picture of a galvanising pot, taken in the early 1940s, shows a finished sheet being stamped with a dolphin, one of the trade marks of Pontnewynydd works, the others being in earlier years, "Coo-ee", "Dome" and "Sable". Also notice the dangerous chain drives to the feed rollers in the pots.

Looking through the gap in the top of the pot, one can see several blocks of Zinc metal ready to replenish the molten zinc in the pot. These pots were coke fired, and some of the coke can be seen on the floor, lower right of the picture.

This photograph shows the packing and dispatch department of the works from where products were dispatched world wide. Some sheets can be seen slung from the overhead crane. The sheets in the foreground had been galvanised and corrugated while the sheets on the rear right of the picture were simply flat galvanised and could be used in the making of numerous items such as buckets etc. Corrugating a sheet gives it extra stiffness for roofing etc.

Many will remember the beautiful cast iron drinking fountain, pictured here, which was installed by the proprietors of the works outside the works gate, at the junction of Hanbury Road and St Luke's Road.

Chapter 9. British Iron Works

Today, when venturing under the Big Arch at Abersychan, one can see the last remnants of a very large ironworks, which had been erected here in 1825.

The British Iron Company's directors, Small, Shears and Taylor, were erecting the ironworks mainly for the manufacture of merchant bars. ("Merchant Bars" comprise various-sized bars used by tradesmen such as blacksmiths etc) This enterprise gave it's name to the district we now know as the British.

From the outset things did not go well, due to unstable ground and flooding on site causing all sorts of problems. Another setback was that management had signed a lease with the Lords and Ladies of the Manor of Wentsland and Bryngwyn, for the use of the land and for the minerals being mined from it. The annual rent along with royalties for every ton of iron produced was to prove so excessive that for the first eleven years no profit from the venture was paid to the shareholders. In 1826, wet weather and the unstable ground had caused a landslide, entailing the building of a large retaining wall, approximately 50 feet high and 800 feet long, behind which the furnaces were being built.

These unforeseen problems saw extra costs for construction of the works escalate greatly to around £75,000 spent, before the first blast furnace had even been fired, or a single house had been completed for its workers; nevertheless, the invention of steam power, revolutionising industries like this one, would see people in their hundreds come to work here, helping to build and run what was to eventually become an enormous undertaking.

This undertaking comprised blast furnaces, steam driven rolling mills, puddling furnaces, collieries, lime kilns and brickworks, etc, employing in excess of 1,300 people at this works alone, thus any surplus housing in the area was soon exhausted.

This caused shanty-like dwellings to spring up everywhere, while the company built row after row of houses close to the site for many of its workers.

Now that the Industrial Revolution was well underway, the shortage of manpower meant that families were flocking to South Wales hoping to find a better life. These poor people came from places such as Ireland looking for employment, and this, combined with the housing shortage, eventually caused much bitterness among the local population, even though these luckless people were, like the local people, living on the lower edges of society; in some cases living twenty to a house and even in some cases "Hot Bedding", i.e. when one man left his bed for his twelve-hour shift, another man climbed into it at the end of his!

Most people will be aware of the unrest in the coal and iron industries in the early to mid-1800s, brought about mainly by the attitude of the ironmasters and the misuse of the power they possessed. As an example of this attitude, the authors quote the following taken from the book *Iron In The Making*, Dowlais Iron Company Letters, 1782–1860, edited by Madeleine Elsas, County Archivist, and published by the county records committee. This first account comes from: *James Brown To Thomas Evans. July 9th 1839. Cwm Celyn & Blaina Iron Works (Monmouthshire)*.

"On the 23rd day of May last a man from Dowlais named Benjamin Phillips applied to me for a situation as over-looker to our blast and other engines which was vacant, & I accordingly entered into a written engagement with him at 35 shillings per week & to commence on the 24th ultimo. A few days since, I sent over to him, when he stated he had entered into a further engagement with you, & that he should not come here at all. What I have to complain of is that he should neglect apprising me of his intentions, there by preventing me from engaging another person who had offered.

"As I have been personally much inconvenienced by this conduct, it is my intention to send him to 'rusticate' for a short period on our Treadmill at Usk or Cardiff, but refrain from doing so until I had communicated with you. If he fills any situation of trust, or is any wise a useful man & such a person as you cannot replace readily, or conveniently spare my "Wrath" will be sufficiently avenged upon the wretch by your frightening him well for his delinquency, but on the other hand, if he is a man that you care little about I will hand him over immediately to the Officers of Justice & then to the executives. I await your reply to the above …"

As such conditions may seem unbelievable today, could the authors point out here the use of the words "our Treadmill!"

We also quote a letter from *Small, Shears Taylor, Abersychan Iron Works, to Guest, Lewis & Co 2nd March 1835:* "Our Colliers having improperly quitted, we beg to enclose a list of their names, & hope that none of them will obtain employment at your works" (list of 202 names).

And this from *James Beaumont Abersychan Iron works to Dowlais Iron Co. 2nd November 1850.* "Will you do us the favour of not allowing any of our men, who are on strike for wages, to be employed in your works, with out their producing a discharge signed by myself, I have not yet heard of any having gone over as far as Merthyr, but should they do so, we should be grateful if you would not employ them without my discharge..."

Today the area of the British is covered with the routes of the old tram roads that served the industries, and in one case the remains of a water balance mine and its structure can still be found on a hillside, with the tops of two further balance pits exposed, and where one is able to observe that one shaft has been built with stone, while the other is brick-lined. All three shafts are of an oval construction, and all sited within view of the works, These water balance mines would have supplied some of the coal and ironstone products needed to make iron at this works.

This 1968 photograph (below) shows the water balance wheel which stood at Cwm Bergwm and was linked by a tram road to the nearby British ironworks. This method of raising coal was only one of several in use at the time; there were also levels and drift mines and also deep mines that were supplying coal and ironstone to these ironworks.

This later photograph shows the balance pithead gear to have been removed, enabling us to view where both cages would come to rest alternately each side of this timber beam. As explained, the balance shafts were mainly of an oval construction; while deeper mineshafts were of round section for strength. The operation of this balance wheel was by way of a cage consisting of a tank of water, the top of which carried tram rails to accommodate a tram. When at the surface, the empty tram was manually pushed into the cage, and the tank filled with water, the weight of which was sufficient to start the cage downward, hoisting the other cage from the shaft bottom with a full tram and empty tank to the surface. Once at pit bottom a full tram was pushed into the cage, and the tank was drained in readiness to complete another cycle. Most balance pits like this one were to be found on high ground, in order that the water when being drained from the tank under the cage could be discharged if possible through natural drainage at the pit bottom; if not, then by small tunnels called adits, cut through the hillsides, which would release the water from pit bottom to a lower level.

Balance wheels were the first attempt to use mechanical power rather than horses or muscle power to raise coal. There were several advantages to this system. As it used no coal or wood fire to generate steam, it was clean and non-polluting, its only by-product being water, and compared with steam, it was also virtually silent.

There is very little now left of our industrial heritage, and what there is is constantly under threat, for example the water balance wheel here at Cwm Byrgwm.

This important artefact – or what is left of it – lies strewn about the mountainside, having been dismantled some years ago. Now, most of it is missing, and will be very difficult to replace, whereas the whole thing ought to have been preserved several years ago, and put on display in a prominent position – preferably on one of the roundabouts at the entrance to town – to serve as a reminder of our true industrial heritage. This industrial heritage goes back a long way, and affected – for better or worse – many ordinary people, who were, in many cases, our direct forebears.

And what was this heritage endured by our forefathers? A life of toil and graft, akin to slavery, even for their children, most of whom were denied for many years even the most basic education.

This photograph overlooks the area of the Cwm Byrgwm site where one can also see the remains of a stack which was part of the Cwm Byrgwm colliery. The reason for taking this photograph is that the authors felt they needed to point out the location where much of the ironstone and coal that was used at the Abersychan works was mined from. The ironworks was located just out of sight, bottom left of this photograph. One other thing we should bear in mind is that wherever we see colliery waste tips such as these, then one should remember that for every ton of spoil that was dumped in heaps like this, then it was probable that on average around ten to twelve tons of coal was removed from below the ground, and indeed due to the timescale when these particular tips were being established in the 1800s, which was before the days of modern mining equipment, for every bit of spoil dumped here, it is fairly certain that it was removed with the use of a shovel, and of course by the sweat of men's brows. During the lifetime of the works there must have been many thousands of tons of coal mined from this area alone, and there were literally dozens of waste tips littering this particular area, many of which have now been removed.

On one of the surrounding hillsides overlooking the British site can be seen a row of ten workmen's houses; Elizabeth Row. This was just one of many rows of houses built here in the early 1820s and 1830s, and now, with so many new people living here, the British was becoming a community in its own right. Thankfully, in the next photograph we can see this same row of houses, which with a great deal of hard work has been restored, and which serves as a reminder of the people and their industry. The restoration work on these houses was carried out by local builder Keith Bones and his wife Margaret.

The same houses in 2007

The American visitor, having spent a night at Abergavenny, had also visited this ironworks on 5 January 1828 after saying: "Next morning (5 January 1828) being Saturday, we found a fine clear morning and the mountain tops all covered with snow and none in the valley. We got breakfast early and started to go up on top of the (Blorenge) Mountain. We went up three or four lifts of the railroad called by the people the incline of the plain (Hill's tram road inclined plane from Llanfoist) and which is very steep, and after leaving it we went up the steep side covered with a long, soft, mossy grass. As we got up we found it quite cold and more snow and ice. When about half way up started a fine hare and gave him a whoop and hallow which started him down the hill in fine style. This was the first hare I ever saw run. The mountain now became very steep and had very toilsome work, but yet I felt it to be very invigorating and took as much pleasure in climbing up after the prospect the mountain was said to afford as any little boy would have done in chasing a butterfly up its side and when we did get to the top we were well paid for our toil as we had a most magnificent prospect, being able to see over a number of counties in England and Wales. Saw the Severn and its shores. The Bristol Channel lay as if it were under us with a great many vessels going to and fro on its bosom. The mountaintops round us all covered with snow, the beautiful green valleys lying below and round us altogether made much the handsomest prospect and scene I ever beheld. On the very top of the mountain is a great heap of stones – some them large – supposed to be an ancient Cairn raised to the memory of some of their ancient chiefs or leaders who were buried there – came slantingly down the side of the mountains and pursued our way on to the British Company's", works saying that he had: "walked up the west of the river through a deep ravine" ("*Bob- a- Day road" was not built at this time*) "where they were building an immense works, Six remarkable large furnaces – Twenty puddling furnaces – and 2 large steam engines are now put up and a larger one is being put up to drive the rolling mills".

From what he had written and from the location of this old engine house, the authors are convinced that the mill engine house referred to has to be the one in this next picture.

To support this theory, the authors also made enquiries as to what engines were purchased for this site, and indeed there were three obtained from the Neath Abbey Iron Company in 1827, which consisted of two fifty-two-and-a-half-inch beam blowing engines which were needed for creating the blast for the furnaces, and one mill engine with a forty-five-inch cylinder and a twenty-foot flywheel.

With the use of the computer, this engine house has been fitted with an engine, and as already explained, is the only one on site at this time. It was built 180 years ago this year, 2007, and although neglected, it remains here still fighting the ravages of time and the elements. As you can see we have modified this picture to show what the engine parts would have looked like when in operation. As can be seen from the picture, there is a beam projecting from the front of the building with a connecting rod leading to a crank on the first motion shaft, which is the shaft the large flywheel is mounted on. The drive to the rolling mills would have been taken through reduction gears, of which the large gear can be seen, mounted on the second motion shaft. As the beam rocked up and down, this motion was converted to a rotary motion by the crank. The square holes seen on the fly-wheel surface were "Barring Holes", so that if the engine stopped on top or bottom dead centre and would not start, the engine driver could, with the use of a bar over a fulcrum, lever the engine from its dead centre position.

Boilers

In order to run these engines, it was necessary to use steam. This was generated by boilers similar to the above one, which is a Lancashire boiler with two fire-tubes, which are closed off in this picture to protect the inside; whereas those in use at the British site in those earlier days would probably have been the Cornish type which would have had a single fire-tube. In order to give the viewer some idea as to the size of these boilers, they measured approximately twenty five to thirty feet long by six to nine feet in diameter, and would again have been similar to these, which there were at least twenty on site. The location of some of these boilers can be seen in the old 1890s photograph just to the right of the beam engine house at low level.

These photographs – taken at the Crofton Pumping Station of the Kennet and Avon Canal Trust – show a boiler under steam, in this case, a Lancashire boiler from a later time.

In this second photograph (above right), one can see, lower left and lower right, flue cleaning doors, while on the boiler front can be seen the two water level gauges and pressure gauge. Also note the two airways under the fire-tubes closed off, in this case because the boiler was only on light duty.

By this time the age of steam was firmly here and saw the end of waterwheels to operate large bellows for supplying blast to the furnaces, for by now they were being replaced with beam blowing engines, where just one single engine could supply sufficient blast for three furnaces.

On 7 January the American returned to the works for a second viewing, and remarked that he "Saw their kiln for making their fire brick, of which all their furnaces etc. are made – took a sample of the material of which they make their brick – and which they grind between a pair of rollers. It is all together a most astonishing works – the engineer is Robert Taylor – the Roller a Mr Jones, and the man who attends the Furnaces, a Mr Naunsket. Their railroad to the canal is of wrought iron rolled and they will make about 500 tons weekly of different kinds of iron."

Note the wheels on this earlier type tram (above), for they were designed to run on the inside of angle iron rails as opposed to the modern wheel which has a flange that runs on the top of flat bottomed-tram rails.

Fire clay is generally grey in colour and composed chiefly of silica and alumina. It is almost always found forming the floor of coal seams and is known as "Under Clay". It is assumed to have been the soil upon which the vegetation now converted into coal flourished. It is usually mined in conjunction with coal, especially thin seams, and is used for making fireclay goods, such as bricks and pipes which resist very high temperatures without melting or becoming soft.

The photograph shown is of an early type tramway sleeper which carried cast iron rails, the size of the stone is given by the one-foot scale ruler.

The sleepy area called Abersychan was by now getting a sudden awakening, for with Pentwyn Iron Works, with its five blast furnaces being erected at the same time by Hunt Brothers, dwellings were also needed for their workers, and indeed they were soon in the process of erecting these dwellings. With large amounts of people now being employed locally, then shops, churches, and eventually schools, had to be built. We say eventually for the majority of the adults and children at that time could not read or write, and for many years to come the only schooling available for many of the children was religious education in Sunday school, with what we would call today "normal education" for them not even considered.

One lad, Patrick Phlin, who worked here in 1842, said: "I think I am near 11 years old and my father is an Irishman. We have been here a long time. I worked in another works before I came here, that was more than a year ago. I help the refiner now at this fire. I have not been at this fire quite a month and I don't know what he will give me. The work is hot sometimes but it is not hard. I like it very well. I have tended masons, it is no harder than that. I go to Sunday School some days but I can't read."

With Elizabeth Row around 130 yards behind where we were standing, we photographed this area from as near the same spot as a photographer had done around 115 years earlier. Looking at the site today, there is little to remind us that an ironworks had ever been erected here, so in order to give an idea of what was located here this image compared with this modern photograph may help one understand particularly where the furnaces were erected.

The rotative beam engine house seen on the bottom left of this photograph is not the one that remains on site, visible through the ghost of the largest chimney, as you can now see; but from the position of the engine house on the left of the picture, its location, and the fact that the boilers can be seen at floor level next to it, then it was probably used for pumping water, being very near to an underground watercourse, and indeed, there is still an entry to this water culvert, complete with an iron ladder in place. One branch of this watercourse appears to be from the stream near Farm Road, (the Sychan Brook), close to the old colliery powerhouse, and also, as can be seen from the next photograph, there is quite a lot of surface water draining to the top of this culvert, and which along with the underground water seems to be draining away quite well, especially since we had had almost non-stop rain for a month. From what we have seen here the problems they had had with unstable ground during erection of the site in the 1820s (due to excess surface water) had now been overcome by good drainage.

When this works was in operation, vast amounts of water would have been needed to feed at least 20 very large boilers, and among the site's other needs would have been water to supply the water-cooled Tuyeres, these would also have used a considerable amount of water. Tuyeres (pronounced "Tweers") were used to inject the air-blast into the furnaces.

There is a report of a happening in July of 1839 due to a great fall of rain. The large pond at Cwmsychan, supplying the Abersychan Iron Works, suddenly gave way around midnight, filling several pits and levels and threatening the destruction of the furnaces.

Two men were drowned, and a third man was saved with difficulty, after being closed up in the workings for two days and nights; fortunately for him, he was in a part of the mine which stayed above water level.

In the picture of the pond, above, the tunnel on the left was the main water outlet, while the breach seen on the right would have been made in recent years to drain the pond for safety reasons. With water being so precious, there would have been other ponds serving the ironworks.

As mentioned above, at the time the photograph of the works was taken, the beam engine house on site today was obscured by the buildings and chimneys in the foreground. The only building recognisable from this photograph is the building barely seen in the distance, which was the Talywain Railway Station goods shed. This whole undertaking, along with its six blast furnaces, seems to stand proud as monuments to the men, women and children that had once worked here, and many of whom also gave their lives to this enormous enterprise.

From these two photographs can be seen the site as it is today, and how it was just before the works had been dismantled. By viewing the plan (next page), it shows that this photograph depicts only a part of what had been erected here

To the top left of this 1880s to 1890s photograph, can be seen the coke ovens that were introduced around 1845; these heated the coal in order to make coke. This process used small coal, fines, etc. rather than lump coal which was too valuable, i.e. it could be sold to both the domestic and industrial markets, much more easily than small coal. Prior to when these ovens were installed, huge piles of large lump coal were fired in the open air, a method which saw up to 43 per cent of its value lost mainly in ash content, as well as losing the valuable by-products to the atmosphere. Coke ovens burned coal in controlled surroundings from which the air was excluded. The heat then expelled the tar and gases which could be used elsewhere, leaving pure coke with less wastage. Across the top of the furnaces can be seen a very large pipe, now partly dismantled, this was the pipe which carried the waste gases from the top of the blast furnaces to heat the coke ovens.

Coke ovens varied in size; briefly, a coke oven was a brick chamber approximately eighteen feet by ten feet by two feet wide, with flues each side. These were heated by blast furnace waste gas. When the coal was fully carbonised, it was pushed out of the ovens by rams and quenched with water.

Two girls, Mary Morgan, aged 17 and Margaret Mark, aged 18, said: "We pile or stack the mine (Ironstone) and we work for a man who has the work. He pays us 6 shillings per week. We have been working two or three years. We go home for dinner as we live in a row of houses close by. We work 12 hours sometimes. We like the work well in fine weather. It is hard enough and we do as much as we can. There are no more girls like us working at this place with us. We build the ironstone up in a heap like a wall as you see it."

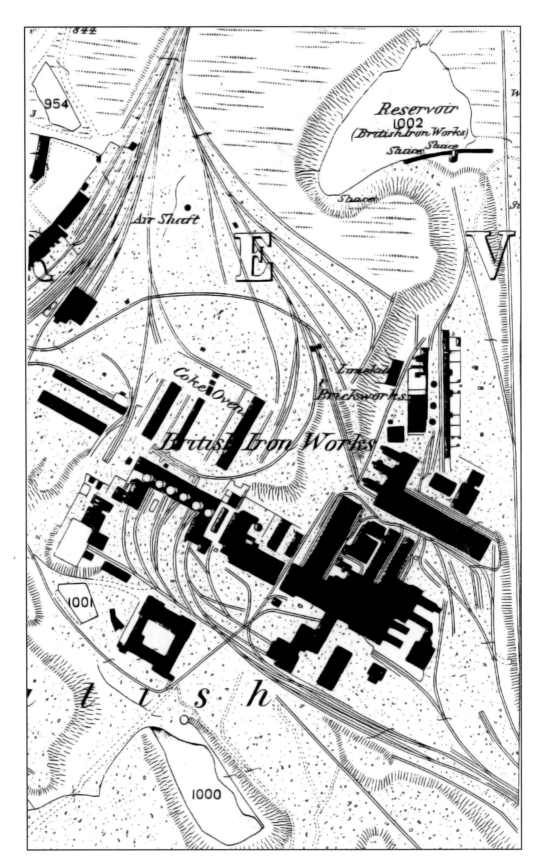

Reservoir
1002
(British Iron Works)
Sluice

954

Air Shaft

E

V

Coke Oven

Langdale Brickworks.

British Iron Works

t i s h

1001

1000

Chapter 10. Workforce

This computer-enhanced photograph gives an idea of what the works would have looked like with the furnaces working at full capacity at the time our American visitor arrived. It was said that the flames would illuminate the sky to such an extent that a newspaper could be read at any time, day or night, but this situation was to alter around 1845 with the fitting of "Cups and Cones" to the top of the furnace. This procedure prevented the escape of the gases from the top of the furnace, allowing them to be piped off for other use, in this case heating the coke ovens, while at the same time the amount of coal needed to produce a ton of pig iron was also considerably reduced.

Cups and cones were used in order to allow for the filling of the furnaces, while preventing the escape of gas while the furnace was in use.

Hot blast was also introduced about this time: this entailed blowing heated air – hot blast – into the furnace, as opposed to cold air. This air was heated by passing it through "Stoves", which were simply an enclosed space in which firebricks were stacked loosely; these were heated by passing waste hot furnace gases through them. This procedure improved the output of the furnace enormously.

Prior to these improvements, it required around four tons of coal to produce one ton of iron, which meant for one week's output of 500 tons of iron being produced, then the amount of coal needed would be 2,000 tons, all of which had to be firstly burned in great piles in the open air in order to produce the coke that was needed to fire the furnaces.

This was a very wasteful method of producing coke, with around 43% of the fuel being wasted. With six blast furnaces here, five at the Pentwyn,

five at Varteg, five at Blaenavon, plus the Golynos ironworks which had three furnaces, then it adds up to 8,000 tons of coal being used per week. This situation, along with extra coal needed for the boilers that produced the steam (22 on this site alone), must have created pollution beyond comprehension. As well as producing coal for local industries the product was being shipped to many different parts of the world, which meant more and more coal mines were opened.

The American visitor mentioned that the buildings at the British were put up and designed in good taste, so by taking a modern-day photograph from just inside the entrance of the big arch, and superimposing another 1840s photo I had onto that one, it will hopefully give an idea of what the American visitor was viewing on that Saturday morning in 1828 (picture above). On the question of who designed the buildings for the ironworks, according to a letter written by R. Nichols, in "A History of the British Ironworks, Abersychan" by Kim Colebrook, we find that it was a famous architect by the name of Decimus Burton, who also drew the plans for the park gates at Hyde Park Corner, the Athenaeum club, Charing Cross Hospital, and much of Kew Gardens; and in fact, an exhibition to commemorate his work on the centenary of his death was held in London in 1981. Mr Nichols remarked: "One wonders how he – Decimus – came to be given the assignment to design an ironworks in the eastern valley of Monmouthshire. Was he or his father (who was also a very well respected London Architect) an acquaintance of one of the entrepreneurs Small, Shears and Taylor? Surely this must be the only industrial enterprise in South Wales to have been designed by such an eminent man!"

After some twenty years or so of variable fortunes, the works was eventually sold in 1852 to the Ebbw Vale Company for £8,641, which was a mere fraction of the sum of £300,000 which had been invested here.

By the 1840s, the railroads were taking the place of the canal systems, thus creating a demand for iron rails, which meant that some light was at the end of the tunnel for the workforce, and also gave the British ironworks another part to play in history. The photograph shows a large pile of iron rails which had probably been produced for both home and export markets, and indeed the rails were being exported to Russia, France, Italy, Spain, Austria, Germany and America. The American pioneers were probably crossing some of their lands on iron rails made here at Abersychan.

"The 1842 Children's Employment Commission, For Inquiring Into The Employment And Condition Of Children In Mines And Manufactories".

The British Iron Company's Works at Abersychan, near Pontypool, were employing about 130 people and making about 400 tons of iron per week, from four furnaces. April 29th.

Total Number of Young Persons and Children Employed.

At the blast furnaces:
9 male young persons and 6 male children.

At the Forges and Mills:
22 male young persons and 8 male children.

At the colliery and mine works:
94 male and 22 female young persons and 78 male and 4 female children.

The youngest children are 1 boy of 5 years, 2 boys of 7 years, 8 boys of 8 years and 11 boys 9 years old at the colliery and mine works.

Summary

	Males	**Females**
Adults	1007	50
Young persons and children	217	26
	1224	76

Total 1300

William Wood Esq. Manager, aged 48 gave the account which follows, in his own words:

"I have been the manager of these works for the last five years and a half. I was previously manager of iron works in North Wales under the same company for nine years, and before that I was several years under Sir John Guest, managing the iron works at Dowlais. I have answered in writing the printed queries sent to this works from the Central Office of the Children's Employment Commission. I am of the opinion that one half of the male children of the working people of this neighbourhood, under the age of 13, are employed in the different works, particularly among the colliers and miners. The furnace men and the forge men have not so many employed. They cannot get employment for as many of their children as they wish. The children are worked in the same way at Dowlais as here, but at North Wales, in the collieries and mines, the children are worked much harder than in this neighbourhood. We work our blast furnaces on Sundays but I do not think it would be any great detriment to their trade generally if all works were to stop their furnaces for eight hours on a Sunday. The quantity of fuel would make no difference in the stoppage. It might be done with all descriptions of fuel which I have used. The coal here is very bituminous and loses between 30 and 40 per cent in coking. We have stopped the blast furnaces here when accidents have occurred for 12 to 18 hours. We had afterwards some trouble to open them but they came round in about 12 hours. The trouble to bring a furnace round into regular work after a stoppage of 8 hours would not be worth speaking of but if the furnace was out of order when it stopped it would be attended with great inconvenience to get it right again. In a well regulated works a furnace may be out of order for one or two days in a month. It would seldom happen that more than one furnace out of four would be out of order on the same day. At our works there is no system of rewards or punishments but the men are occasionally fined for neglect of duty and for drunkenness. The fine is 2s. 6d. for each offence. The fines are carried to a fund called the "Sick fund". There is now about £200 in balance of this fund unappropriated. It was formerly applied, in small weekly payments to cases of sickness but that application of this money is abandoned. The fines at these works amounts to about seventy pounds per annum among 1300 men. We do not profess to keep any holidays excepting Christmas Day, but all our works except the blast furnaces are stopped in consequence of the men being drunk mostly two or three days at Christmas and also Easter Monday which is generally a day for club feasts. In a conversation I had with Mr Wood on the subject of the fines levied upon the workmen, he informed me that he had proposed to apply the money then standing on the books to the credit of the sick fund, to the purpose of building a school house, and he expressed his opinion that if a system of fines was legalised at all works (such a system being already very generally practised) a fund might thus be provided which would, with very little additional aid from the masters or other sources, efficiently maintain a school at each establishment."

With regard to these views, when this man mentions drunkenness in the workforce, the authors would like to point out that it was not necessarily the men who were to blame, since they were receiving part of their wages in ale, and to add to this ludicrous situation, the men were now being fined for drinking part of what were their wages, as well as being fined for "Neglect of duty and drunkenness". The fines mentioned above then being credited to a sick fund with a view to building a school house, "with very little aid from the Iron masters or other sources". In short, it was the workforce, already underpaid, and not the ironmasters, who were doing the paying yet again!

11. Transport

The works was to suffer its ups and downs on a regular basis, and was often in trouble due to the fluctuating price of iron, resulting in workers being on short time, or laid off, due to only two, or even at times just one, of its six blast furnaces operating. The consequences of this meant that families who were already short of the basic needs of life, food, clothing, etc. were now reduced to even lower living standards, and it was thanks to the foresight of those who set up soup kitchens for the needy – and particularly the children – that many of these people survived at all.

Now that the works was in the hands of the Ebbw Vale Company, the management set about upgrading its transport system

by erecting an inclined plane from Talywain to Twyn-y-Ffrwd to connect at Cwmffrwd with the Blaenavon tram road, later to become the railway.

On the right of the photograph can be seen the Victoria School with the playground in front, which was not built until 49 years later in 1902. What stands out from this picture is the lack of vegetation close to the tram roads, and even though the tram road had not been use since the late 19th century, this may still have been due to polluted ground.

This incline was operated by a stationary engine situated near "Bleak House" but the system proved to be very slow and costly to operate.

Transport for the iron and coal was by means of tram roads that were to link up with the canal at Pontnewynydd, just opposite to where St Luke's church stood.

Photographs courtesy of Mr Terry Targett.

Monmouthshire railway and
Canal Co. Pontnewynydd Arm.

The location opposite St Luke's Church, now demolished, was the terminus of the Pontnewynydd Arm of the canal, and would have been a considerable width, in fact a "Basin", in order that barges could be turned for the return journey. This computer-generated photo gives just an idea as to what the canal at Pontnewynydd may have looked like at that time, with thousands of tons of iron being dispatched, mainly to Newport from this loading point. The canal would have served such places as the Pentwyn Iron Works – Five Furnaces, British Iron Works – Six Furnaces, Golynos Iron Works, three Furnaces, Varteg Iron Works – Five Furnaces, and prior to the opening of the Brecknock and Abergavenny Canal, Blaenavon's iron – Five Furnaces – would also have been loaded here.

The weir shown in this photograph supplied, via the sluice shown on the left, the holding pond for Pontypool New Town Forge. In order to obtain water, the canal feeder would have been taken from behind a weir similar to the one shown above. The sole purpose of a weir in this case, was to raise the water level of the river so that it could be diverted into a feeder, whether for replenishing the canal, or to drive a water wheel, and the feeder tunnel shown in the next photograph would have operated the same way, but in this case the weir is no longer in place.

The tunnel seen in this picture, on the far bank of the river was the feeder which supplied water to the canal terminus near St Luke's Church.

To return to the British Iron Works; although there were many good years still to be had for the industry, the more modern processes of making iron and steel, such as the Bessemer system, invented in 1856, which could produce steel at a lesser cost, along with subsequent strikes and depressions in the industry, helped to bring about the inevitable end to a once enormous enterprise.

During times of great depression at the British Iron Works, which were numerous, its workforce was set to work building a roadway up from Abersychan, and as these photographs show, much of the furnace slag from the site was used in the road construction, and later for packing around the stonework of the Big Arch with the coming of the Great Western Railway in 1879.

Production at the British Iron Works ceased in 1882, with the final closure in 1884. The works were then demolished in 1891.

Big Arch

Bob a day road

Because the rate of pay for building the roadway was one shilling per man per day (a shilling being a bob), the roadway was to become known, as it still is today, as the "Bob a Day".

These offices and outbuildings, beam engine house plus the remains of the Cwmbyrgwm balance wheel, are all that remain here now as part of what was for its time an enormous undertaking.

Offices and out buildings

Chapter 12. Social History

These images from: The Illustrated London News and the Graphic

With chimney stacks, furnaces and other steam-driven machines constantly belching out smoke and fumes, the air would have been filled with a great deal of pollution, leaving just about everything covered with a layer of grime, so that it would have been a difficult task trying to keep both home and family clean under such conditions, not to mention the dire effect on people's health; but another more important factor in workers' lives was this: when colliery buildings and ironworks were being erected, it is obvious from the ornate stonework and the quality machinery used, that no expense was spared, for only the best that money could buy was installed at these places. Yet, inside these buildings, there were many unguarded machines in these workplaces, with little or no regard being paid to the workers' safety whatsoever.

This cost men, women and children the loss of limbs, sight and even life itself. It can only be concluded that where this sort of thing was happening then it seems that many owners of such places had little or no regard at all for their workers.

This statement is borne out by the following list, for the first casualty of the British ironworks was to take place in its very first year of production, with one Richard Lewis falling from the top of a blast furnace. In April 1846 a lad named Jones was drawn through the rolling mills and killed while trying to retrieve his hat. In August 1852 John Ball was killed by an unprotected flywheel. In June 1856, ten-year-old Lewis Edmunds was crushed to death in machinery. In September 1856 George Caples was killed in a rail cutting machine; that very same day Sarah and Joseph West were both scalded to death when a steam pipe burst, while just two weeks later Stephen Garrett was literally cut in half when falling onto a circular saw. In May 1857, Thomas Dawkins was crushed by a cinder tram, Richard Combs was killed by becoming entangled in a clay mill, and so on, with the list claiming lives for almost every year until the works closure in 1884.

Scenes like this were commonplace due to the amount of people being killed at any one time, in both the iron and coal industries.

"The murmuring poor, who will not fast in peace"
Henry David Thoreau. 1817 – 1862

Punch magazine 1852.

The Coming of the Unions

Most people will be aware of the unrest in the coal and iron industries in the early to mid-1800s, brought about mainly by the attitude of the ironmasters. As an example of this attitude, and the power they possessed at the time, the authors quote the following taken from the book *Iron In The Making*, Dowlais Iron Company Letters, 1782–1860, edited by Madeleine Elsas, County Archivist, and published by the County Records Committee. Included in the above book are many letters between the various ironmasters on the subject of Trade Unions.

The following letter gives the Church's attitude to the budding Trade Union Movement:

"A plain address to such members of the union lodges as are in connection with Christian Churches" by Thomas Revel Guest:

"...Take heed and beware of covetousness, so that in providing for your own house you are not to infringe on the providential order of God, by invading the rights of others, by attempting to force upon those whom God has set over you, the adoption of such regulations and the payment of such wages as would be beneficial to yourselves while they would be ruinous to your masters. Here then the Union Societies completely oppose one branch of that commandment on which hangs all the law and the prophets, viz. 'Thou shalt love thy neighbour as thy self', besides convicting of that spirit of covetousness of which we are exhorted to be beware and take heed. It will be enough to remind you that Satan sometimes transforms himself into an angel of light to deceive the brethren to lead them to destruction. Is not this union a confederacy that brings you into those places where as men fearing God you should not be found, The public house is not the usual place of resort for the Disciples of Christ, that is not the place where prayer is wont to be made, where your fathers name is honoured..."

In the first half of the 19th century, most workers only earned meagre wages in these works and collieries, and wages in many cases were being paid in tokens that could only be spent in company shops at inflated prices. This was the "Truck shop system", which caused much unrest, and saw people trying to form what would eventually become Trade Unions.

As the influx of people continued, it soon became evident that there were too few jobs for the amount of workers available, so the colliery owners and so-called ironmasters could pick and choose who they wanted to employ at cheap rates, and who they would lock out. Some of these owners and managers did this with great zeal, until workers realised they needed to unite and fight, a situation which was vigorously combated by magistrates, who were really the same employers in a different guise, and it was they who were passing harsh sentences in order that they could keep control over the workers. In fact, a law was passed: "The General Combination Acts", which were designed to stop "any two people from combining together in order to gain higher wages or a decrease in working hours". Anyone breaking this act would find themselves spending a three-month spell in one of His Majesty's jails, providing it was his or her first offence, but more severe punishments would follow if a second breach occurred. Employers refused to employ anyone who partook in the unions in any form and if caught, they, the so-called culprits, were locked out of the industry. But of course, this sort of practice by the employers only drove unions underground, to emerge and become known as "Scotch Cattle", who had members in almost every iron industry in the locality, and anyone who did not support them in their quest would be paid a visit by these Scotch Cattle, who would break into the dissenter's house and destroy or burn many of their possessions, and indeed this happened to at least one dwelling in Abersychan.

In 1822 a strike was called in Pontypool, which lasted 13 weeks, until the employers agreed to increased wages and the abolition of the truck system.

But still the unjust actions of the mine and landowners continued, until eventually the situation saw further trouble as a result of The Poor Law Amendment Act in 1834, whereby any able-bodied man would not be allowed to claim any benefits such as parish relief, which in effect was to see the individual deprived of the means of sustenance. But fortunately, there were men in the land who had the determination to do all in their power to break this dominance of the ruling classes, and set up what became the Chartist Movement, which would combat unjust treatment and laws which benefited the ruling classes only. Locally, one of the Chartists, one Vincent, was arrested, and as a protest a march to Newport was organised and led by three men, John Frost of Newport, Zephaniah Williams from Abergavenny, and William Jones of Pontypool. The march ended in tragedy, with 22 Chartists left dead after being shot by troops from the windows of the Westgate Hotel, and although this action was to culminate in the three leaders of the Chartist movement being sentenced to death (later commuted to transportation to Tasmania), the movement had set the precedent which in years to come would succeed in breaking the stranglehold of the upper classes, even though injustice and greed often still rears it ugly head. These men had put their lives on the line, ensuring that everyone today has the right to make his or her own decisions, and the right to withdraw his or her labour, and to build a fairer society which is right and just for all.

Perhaps this drawing from an 1865 French magazine "Le Tour De Monde", of women workers at Cyfartha Iron Works at Merthyr Tydfil, depicts the condition of workers of the time, and stands as a reminder to us all for it seems that theirs was a dismal "hand to mouth" existence. Today we cannot even imagine just how hard things must have been for these people. There is little wonder that riots were commonplace, or that the earlier 1839 Chartist Movement had so many supporters.

Sometimes today we hear much disparaging talk against the unions, but perhaps it should be remembered that it was such injustices as these which bought the unions into being initially.

Some of the social consequences of the iron industry, in this case the tin-plate trade, are graphically illustrated in the following article.

Thomas Morgan Wintle, who was a native of Pontnewynydd, started work with his father and learned the trade of Roll-Turner, after which he worked for W.T. Henley, at Pontnewynydd works, after they were modified for the manufacture of wire rods for cable-making. After some time away, Thomas retuned to Pontymoile with his wife, Helen, in a cottage in what was – and is – known as The Old Estate Yard. Walking along the canal one evening,

they saw something which altered their outlook on life: there were many neglected children in this area, so they decided to set up a "Ragged School". Within a few days, they had converted a disused granary in the Old Estate Yard into a meeting house, complete with benches.

With gifts of sweets – an action that would certainly be misconstrued in our enlightened days – Mr Wintle gathered about twenty ragged and barefoot boys from the ironworks, the canal bank, and the riverside fields. So popular did these meetings become – with both children and adults – that the small room they had was not large enough, so about June 1880, they built another one of steel sheets not far away, near what was Great Western Terrace.

Soon, this hall too was inadequate for their needs, and so they built another, larger one of stone; and this hall lasted until recently, when it too was demolished to make way for the new road. The land that hall was built on belonged to the Ebbw Vale Steel, Iron and Coal Company, whose lease had still twenty years to run. The young Missionary approached them, and to his delight was told they would forego their lease, which was held from Mr J.C. Hanbury, of Pontypool Park. On approaching Mr Hanbury, he was told he could lease the land, and Mr Hanbury went further, and consented to a lease of 99 years at a nominal rent of one shilling per annum!

In the early days of his ministry, Mr Wintle came face to face with the terrible suffering of the poor in the Eastern Valley. For twenty-seven weeks in the winter of 1885/86, more than 30,000 meals were provided for both children and adults, and during the following winter, more than 20,000 were provided.

In 1893, another bad time followed. The tin-plate industry was ruined by the McKinley Tariff (an import tax imposed by an American, one Mr McKinley) and a week before Christmas 1894, between four and five thousand people were deprived of the means of sustenance.

Mr Wintle established free meals for the children first, and adults after, and for 42 weeks this relief continued. In the 16 months from August 1893, more than 100,000 free meals were provided for the starving and unemployed, and 1,600 Christmas dinners were provided in their own homes. Mr Wintle died at the home of his daughter and son-in-law, at Wyre Court, Bewdley, and his remains were brought back to his home, "Bethany" at Pontymoile, on Tuesday, 9 March, 1926. His funeral left the Mission Hall on Pontymoile at 2.33 pm on the following Friday, and there were so many people wishing to pay their respects that the cortege didn't reach Panteg cemetery, half a mile away, until after dark. So many people wished to act as bearers that the coffin was passed forward from group to group most of the way to the cemetery and there were hundreds of men, women and children at the funeral, mostly Mission members.

The new mission hall on Rockhill Road, Pontypool

We have many roads in the district named after prominent people of the district, but is it not time that we had a monument – perhaps a road or close – named after such a man as Thomas Morgan Wintle?

Chapter 13.
Varteg, Blaenavon and Mining

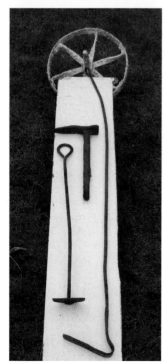

Many people will be aware of the location of Forge Row Cwmavon, but few will be aware of the reason for the name "Forge Row". It was because of the forge situated opposite – Varteg Forge – established in around 1802, and from the site of which this photograph was taken. It seems that this site received iron from both Blaenavon and Varteg furnaces for refining and conversion into bar iron. There have been artefacts recovered from the site (illustrated) by the present owners, Mr and Mrs Price.

We were also informed by Mr and Mrs Price that there had been a file factory on this site, and indeed they have recovered many files in various sizes on site.

To the north of the site, on the river, a weir can still be seen that supplied a holding pond for a water wheel, which in turn created the power which operated the site machinery.

We were also told that in 1976 there were still "ovens", possibly puddling furnaces, which could explain the large amounts of slag still scattered around the site.

It may be asked why this was called Varteg forge, when it is located in Cwmavon. We, the authors, have been unable to find the reason.

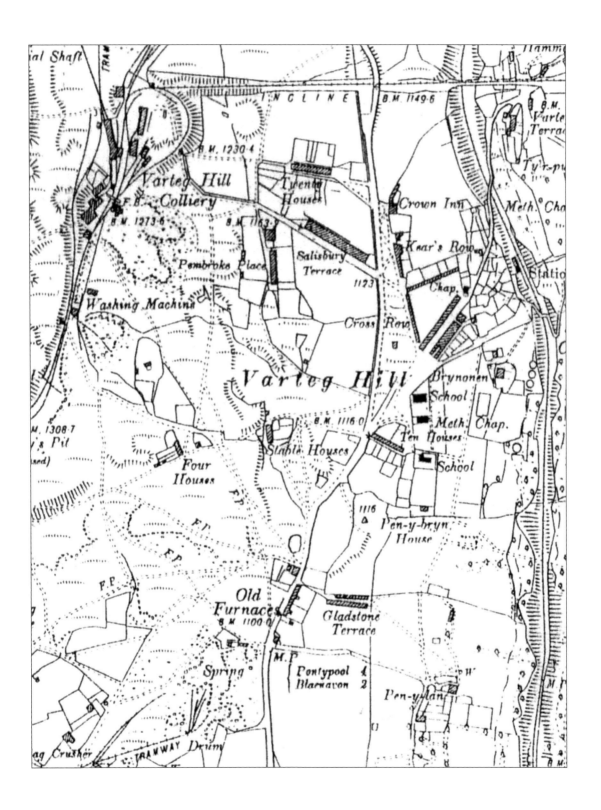

Varteg

At the bottom centre of the map on the previous page can be seen the location of the Varteg ironworks (marked old furnaces) where can be seen the incline that ran from near Gladstone Terrace down to the valley bottom and probabaly serving the Varteg forge and Cwmavon and also another inclined way can be found from the Varteg collieries to the valley bottom.

It seems that the Varteg iron works at one time had 5 furnaces and when the American visited there in January 1828, he remarked that: "It is a very large iron works where there are a great deal of puddling factories and where they make a great deal of iron bars, and round rods etc, in the rolls by steam power and a 20 foot wheel by water which works a forge hammer.

"While here the rain came on so heavy we were obliged to put about – stopped at a Tavern where we hoped to get something to eat and a bed for the night, but after remaining until near night, found upon inquiry we could have only bread and cheese to eat and no bed for any price, so although it was raining very hard, and near night, we were obliged to turn out and walk nearly four miles to Pontypool, and having but one umbrella with us and not coats, we were, upon our getting to our Inn, tolerably well wet."

The Varteg works was one of the oldest in the area, having been established in 1803, so pack mules and horses would have been used for transporting the iron and the power of water would have been needed for their bellows etc.

The next picture shows the inclined plane from the Varteg collieries to Cwmavon, but the only thing to be seen today of this inclined plane is the route.

This incline was erected in the 1850s for the purpose of lowering coal from the Varteg collieries to the valley bottom and then to be transported on the railway line from Pontypool to Blaenavon. The principle of the incline's operation was by the use of a stationary engine, which saw full trams being lowered while at the same time returning empty trams up.

The Cwmavon site and its houses are said to be very important, due to them probably having been operated by the first ironmasters of the Blaenavon Ironworks.

As we are dealing with the Varteg ironworks at this point, extracts taken from the book *Iron In The Making*, Dowlais Iron Company Letters, 1782–1860, edited by Madeleine Elsas, County Archivist, and published by the County Records Committee, seem relevant:

George Smith Kenrick, manager of the Varteg Hill Iron Works, to one Josiah John Guest, dated August 30th, 1831:

"...I agree with you that the Miners Union has a most mischievous tendency. If the men are suffered to establish their union upon a regular system, nothing but confusion and violence can be expected, and it is better that the evil should be crushed in the bud. The unions have not spread to such an extent here as at Merthyr, but I found that thirty of the colliers and miners had joined it about a fortnight ago, and I gave them notice to leave, and that plan I have continued to pursue with them. I believe not one of our firemen is yet engaged, and it is my intention to let them know that if they join the union they will inevitably lose their situation at these works, and I trust they will keep themselves clear of the contagion.

I have called upon Mr Hill and Mr Hunt, (*Blaenavon and Pentwyn Iron works managers*), and their views nearly coincide with my own as to the importance of the subject; and that whatever measures are adopted should be followed up at all events, for any triumph on the part of the men at this moment would cement the union so that it would resist all our efforts in the future. Mr. Hunt and Mr. Hill were both willing to concur in any general measure and it was agreed that the latter should see Mr. Bailey on the subject as we consider him to belong to our district..."

In fairness to this man, we, the authors, would also like to bring to the reader's attention the following facts:

The manager of the Varteg works at the time of the American's visit, was a man who, by the time he had left the ironworks in 1841, having been manager for 16 years, had gained a reputation as being one of the most upright of all the South Wales Ironmasters. He was George Smith Kenrick (1803–1848). Considering what has been written about the Iron Masters of the time, then this was a very high compliment to be paid indeed. George was only 46 when he died, and had suffered the loss of his first wife, who had died in childbirth, so he was also a man who had suffered despair. George had done much in the area and, having been described as a caring man, he believed in education and had set up a school, a mechanics institute and a reading society and was, in short, said to be a man with a vision and above all else it seems that from his actions that he cared for his fellow man.

We have included here cases of children's employment from various places round Wales, as there was little, if any, variation in the working conditions for them.

This next extract was taken from the Children's Employment Commission of 1842.

No.15. Thomas Orndel, aged 12. I am a helper at the top of the furnace. I have been two years at the work and I get 5s. 6d. per week. My work is not hard when the furnace is going slow. I work 12 hours and work at night every other week. I get plenty to eat dinner, sometimes more than an hour but not regularly. The day and night work is the same, I don't care which. I go to school on Sunday sometimes but cannot read.

No.16. John Bowse, aged 11. I fill stone at the top of the furnace. I have worked a long time. I don't know how long. I don't know what I get. I help the man who does the work. I don't work very hard.

The Coal Industry: Deep Mines

In previous chapters, the authors have referred to the use of coal, and when Abraham Darby found that coal, when carbonised into coke, was a far more efficient fuel for use in iron-making, the need for coal grew considerably, and meant that a way of mining deeper seams of coal became necessary. Now that the age of steam had arrived, with, for example, the Newcomen atmospheric pumping engine, mines could now be kept free of water, and it was the brilliant James Watt who eventually turned this primitive engine into a more efficient double-acting rotative beam engine using live steam, which was now suitable for both pumping and winding.

Construction and farming industries could also benefit from the new-found source of power. Steam could power locomotives for the railway systems, and ships could be propelled quicker. Once recognised by men with money, steam was being harnessed all over the world to power the newly emerging industries. In short, the world could now go faster; but this speed would come at a heavy price in both life and limb, because deep mines were an entirely different proposition, and posed problems and dangers as yet undreamt of.

But first, the mines had to be sunk by men called sinkers, who would sink a shaft mainly by hand using a large bucket or "Bowk" on a sinking hoist, as seen in the photograph.

This was also a very dangerous job, with fatalities and injuries being commonplace, many of which was caused by objects, such as stones, tools, etc., falling down the shaft, men falling from the sinking bowk or skip, or occasional cave-ins while sinking through loose strata. After the shaft had been sunk to a certain depth the ground was then levelled and a cast iron ring was placed around the circumference of the shaft and wedged into place,

and on this the first section of brickwork would be laid and tied into the rock strata. Once this brick-work had set, and the next section of shaft had been dug out, this ring would then be removed and refitted lower down, and a further section would be bricked up and married into the first section. When the shaft was 60 to 80 feet deep, it became necessary to make arrangements for the circulation of fresh air to where the men were working. Sometimes wooden boxes around 12 inches square were fitted to the shaft wall to form a pipe, while at the top a cowl was fitted with its open end turned into the wind. The wind pressure then forced the air down to the bottom of the shaft, from where it returned up the shaft. When no wind was available then a hand-operated fan was fitted. This same principle would be applied right down to the bottom of the finished shaft. In most cases a water garland (a cast iron trough built into the brickwork around the full circumference of the shaft) was also fitted to collect any water running down the shaft walls to one place for removal. This process would then continue until the shaft was at the required depth.

The next step would be the erection of permanent pithead gear and engine house, as shown in the photograph of Pontypool Glyn Pits on the next page, plus the necessary buildings, such as boiler house, blacksmith shop, tram repair shed, and necessary tram lines. The Glyn Pits was erected here by Capel Hanbury Leigh in 1845, and would have been one of the first mines in Wales to have used steam as its main power.

The winding ropes in the picture may look oversized; this is because they were flat woven ropes, as round ropes were not extensively used in the early days of mining. For further information on this important site of Pontypool Glyn Pits, go to www.pontypoolglynpits.co.uk.

Ventilation

In a deep mine such as we have described here there were usually two shafts, designated the "Up-cast" and "Down-cast" shafts. Foul air and gases were exhausted from the mine via the up-cast shaft. The heat from a furnace (near pit bottom)– shown opposite – was used to heat the air in the up-cast shaft, thus making the column of air lighter, causing it to rise. This was known as the "Motive Column". This then drew fresh air from atmosphere into the mine through the down-cast shaft, which after traversing the mine workings left by way of the up-cast In later days this procedure was carried out by means of a fan.

In order to avoid mine gases – which could be explosive – coming into contact with the flames of the furnace, a "Dumb Drift" was used.

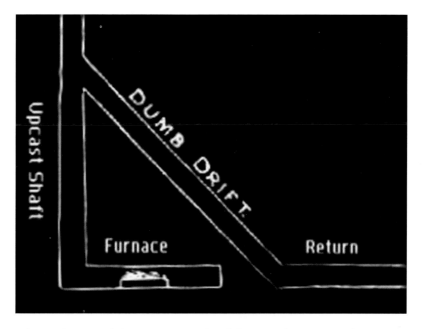

This was simply another tunnel driven up an angle of about 45 degrees into the up-cast shaft, carrying the foul air from the mine to a higher point in the up-cast shaft, thus preventing any chance of ignition from the furnace.

This photograph shows the rotor of a "Sirocco" type mine ventilating fan. This was comparatively small compared to later, more modern types of fan.

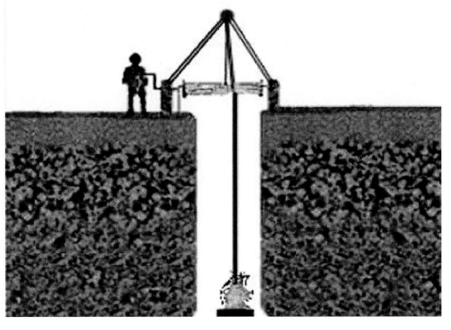

In some cases fire baskets were used. These were simple "Braziers", or large baskets of fire suspended in the up-cast shaft from an overhead framework or simple cantilever bracket by a chain attached to a "Windlass" or small hand-operated winch.

These fire baskets were usually lowered into the shaft at the end of the shift and removed at the commencement of work the following day, by which time the column of air in the shaft would have been warmed, thus helping to circulate the air through the mine. As we have stated above, this was known as the "Motive Column".

This photograph was taken at pit bottom around 1908. The man on the right was called the "Onsetter", who was in charge of loading the cages with either trams of coal or men at pit bottom, and would signal to the surface accordingly. Signalling was carried out by the use of a bell located on the centre of the overhead beam in the photograph. As can be seen there are men about to ascend the shaft, while the other cage is at the pithead.

Prior to an act of 1842, which disallowed women and also children from working underground, these people were regularly used in mining to increase the output of coal and ironstone from mines, and it was commonplace for a woman when underground to be wearing a harness with a chain taken between her legs and attached to a sledge, on which was mounted a basket of coal. Usually a boy or a young girl would be helping to move the sledge by pushing and steadying it from behind.

Even very young children were used to enhance the output of coal, and one of these children in later years reminisced about his underground experiences by remembering how one morning his father had called him out of bed in the early hours to start work as a door attendant in the mine – the boy was just six years old. He also remembered that his father had carried him on his back to the colliery, where they descended the shaft to the pit bottom. After a lengthy walk through the tunnels, they came to an air door which was used to divert ventilation to where it was needed, and was to be the boy's place of work. His father explained that he was to open and close the door when a haulier with his horse and tram passed through.

Before leaving for his own place of work, the father cut, with a mandrel (small pick), a recess from between two upright timbers which were supporting the roof. He had done this in order that his son had somewhere to retire to in safety, because many children were being maimed or killed when falling asleep in the path of the horses and trams. Also before leaving, the father gave his son several candles to last him to the end of the shift.

But the one thing the boy remembered above all else was that after a short time he suddenly became startled by a menacing voice of an official saying: "Don't you go to sleep now, for I shall be back to check up on you later." Just imagine what fear was inflicted on a child of just six years old, yet believe it or not, this child was one of the lucky ones, for a lot of parents could not afford the price of a candle, which meant their child or children would be in total darkness for the whole shift, except when a haulier came by with a lamp. The only sound was that of rats scurrying around in their quest for food.

Another job for women was winding men, women and coal to the surface with the use of a windlass, which was a hand-operated winch, as seen in the illustration of a firebasket being lowered into the shaft. Women were used regularly to do this work and indeed they were known as "Windlass Girls".

In early deep mines, ventilation was primitive, and had always been a problem in mines, with danger in the form of gases, such as firedamp (methane, CH_4), which would always be present. If we turned the clock back a hundred and twenty years or so, we would have found a man clad in water-soaked sacking lying at floor level, holding a long stick with a lit candle on the end, which he would insert into any cavity which he thought may contain gas. The reason for this almost suicidal performance was to burn off any gas present before the miners started their shift, as any build-up of gases would have to be removed, and this was simply the best method they knew of removing it. It is from this method of testing for gas that the fireman was so-called. Gas in coal mines, along with naked lights, such as candles and oil lamps, was always going to be a cocktail for disaster, and indeed when reading the death lists of people killed in British coal mines, it is hard to imagine that this sort of carnage took place. In many cases the death list numbered hundreds of lives at any one time; in fact the list is so long it would take a book of many pages in itself to list the dead.

The largest single mining death toll in a Welsh coal mine was at the Universal Colliery, Senghenydd, which took the lives of 81 miners 24 May 1901, and then again 12 years later 14 October 1913, where the death toll reached an unbelievable 439 lives. The deaths from these two disasters added up to 520 miners, and is to this day the largest loss of life in any one British coal mine. However, there was also a heavy loss of life in local collieries, in particular the Llanerch Colliery disaster of 1890.

The Llanerch Colliery, formerly known as Cwmnantddu (Valley of the Black Stream), was situated at Cwmfrwddoer, Pontnewynydd, and just a mile or so from Abersychan, and it was here on the morning 6 February 1890 that Walter Jones, a surface worker, heard the sound of a massive explosion that was followed by billowing smoke from the pit shaft; he said that "the sound from the explosion leaving the shaft was like that of a discharge from a cannon".

Llanerch Colliery

By 11 am the first bodies began to arrive at the pithead, by which time friends and relatives were at the mine waiting for news of their loved ones, while underground, rescuers were dealing with an area called "Cook's Slope", where the explosion had originated with devastating results. Bodies of men and horses were in many cases being found with limbs missing and badly burned, and in some cases men were mutilated beyond recognition. Almost every family in the locality had lost a member or at least a friend.

At Prince of Wales colliery, Abercarn, on 11 Sept 1878, 268 died in an explosion, and in order to try and control the resulting underground fire, water was poured down the shafts; in fact, they turned the local canal into the mine, but to no effect as far as the trapped men and animals were concerned, with the result that most of those miners and their horses rest in the mine workings to this day. At Risca Black Vein 1 Dec. 1860, 146 died and at Risca new mine 120 died in 1880.

The list is endless, with the final total running into many thousands of lives, both adult and children, before it was realised that coal dust was responsible for the increasing severity of the explosions.

When a mine explosion took place, it was not only the gas that exploded; the explosion was enhanced by fine coal dust, which was lifted from the floor and anywhere the dust may have settled, such as mine timbers etc. Explosions of this kind were caused by a build up of "Fire Damp", which as mentioned is chiefly the gas methane CH_4. Besides which, coal dust, being flammable, and fine, also presented a large surface area, which was conducive to flame propagation through the mine workings. This explosion, besides physical damage, also removed most of the oxygen from the air, leaving nitrogen, carbon monoxide and carbon dioxide, non of which will support life.

Most of these explosions were caused by either a naked light or sparks from tools on rock or other metal.

The Davy Lamp

It was Sir Humphrey Davy who first found a solution to this situation.

Davy realised that surrounding the flame of a lamp with copper gauze cooled the products of combustion before they came into contact with mine gases, but although used for many years, this lamp was not very effective at lighting the workplace.

It was a Dr William Reed Clanny who added a glass to the lamp, thus increasing the light output greatly, and it remains virtually the same lamp to this day.

It was said by mine owners that the miners preferred candles for the extra light they gave, while at the same time, it was said by miners that management would not purchase lamps due to the cost.

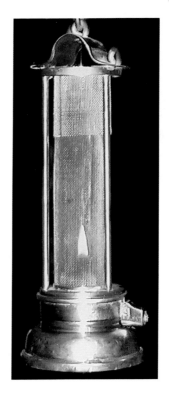

The truth probably lay somewhere between these two views, as some miners probably did prefer the extra light from a candle, but it must be realised that the final decision on mine regulations rested with the mine owners.

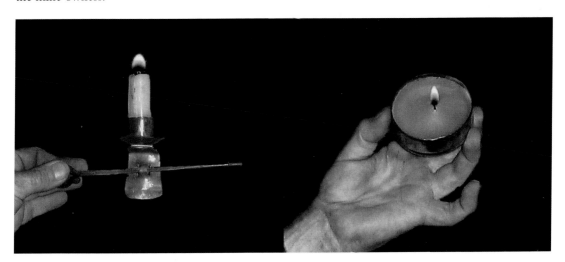

The following pictures show some of the types of lamp used in mining from early times until the present day.

These pictures show two types of candles. The candle on the left could be described as "normal", while the candle on the right is home-made, as occasionally made using fat from the Sunday joint; the drawback with this type of light was the awful smell.

The following two photographs show two oil lamps where one is designed to be fixed as close as possible to the place of work, with the spike on the holder usually driven into the nearest pit prop, while the other one is a cap lamp that in this case has a cover over the wick which is replaced when the lamp is not in use, as seen here. The following two photographs are of a carbide cap lamp. Carbide – properly calcium carbide – is made by fusing together coke and lime in an arc furnace. The lamp is manufactured in two halves, the bottom half contains the carbide, while the top half contains water. When the water is released through a valve onto the carbide, acetylene gas is generated, which burns with a brilliant white light.

The lamp seen in this photograph is fitted with a "Bonnet", which meant that the gauze in the lamp was protected from draughts, which was a failing of earlier types, in that they could easily be blown out. Further, this lamp takes its air from the top of the bonnet, so that when held up into a roof cavity, it drew in any gas present in the cavity with its combustion air, causing a blue cap to appear on the flame. The height of this cap, to a practised eye, would indicate the per centage of gas present, if any.

It will also be noticed that the lamp has a locking mechanism. This was to prevent the lamp – for safety reasons – being opened by other than officials , such as firemen, overmen or management.

This next passage of text was taken, with kind permission, from Mr Brian Foster's book *A Tribute to the Eastern Valley Colliers and Miners 1800–1900*.

"During the 1898 coal strike terrible distress was felt throughout the whole of the Eastern Valley, with bread being distributed every day at Blaenavon, and soup kitchens being opened in every town and village. Owing to a shortage of funds, the soup kitchens at Garndiffaith and Abersychan were forced to stop relief for adults, and concentrate their efforts on local children, while at Pontypool bread and cheese were given three times a week to the most needy cases.

"People at Pontnewynydd were marginally more fortunate, receiving not only bread and cheese, but also cocoa, which was donated by Messrs Cadbury Bros. Some Pontnewynydd families were also given evaporated milk, although the Free Press emphasised that 'In all relief centres, only the most deserving cases need apply.'"

No book on local ironworks could be complete without incorporating in its pages some of the history of the Iron Works at the World Heritage site at Blaenavon, and to view what is left of a great ironworks. It was built by three men, Thomas Hill, Benjamin Pratt, and Isaac Pratt in 1787, where, like at Abersychan, they had taken advantage of the hillside in order that the materials could be fed into the top of the furnaces with relative ease. Today the works' remains stand as monuments to these three men's foresight and the ingenuity of the Blaenavon people.

Much has been restored to a point where we can see and imagine just what it was like to have worked here.

As you know, while writing this book we have been following the visit of an American, James Ramsey Patterson, who in fact came from Beaver Falls, Pennsylvania.

He was on a journey around the British Isles with the intention of gathering information on the details of tin plate manufacture. The idea was to set up a tin plate works in Pennsylvania, and as part of his journey he arrived at Blaenavon on the afternoon of 3 January 1828. He said that he was surprised to see such an immense works set out before him, and summed up what he was viewing in the following words:

"There are five furnaces in a range of great size, and are more like prestigious castles than anything else, and are built on the side of the mountain. They have a very beautiful steam engine made at Neath Abbey, of 55 inch cylinder, and the air pump twice that in diameter, which blows four furnaces, four carbonating hearths, and seven or eight black smith fires with one furnace always being under repair.

"The iron ore and coal are all gathered together in the side of the mountain, and it is really astonishing to see the numerous rail roads and tunnels, some of which run up to three quarters of a mile. Great piles of coal burning into coke and the fires of ore roasting, the fires and smoke of the steam engines and furnaces etc, make the place look like a Vulcan chief's workshop."

Perhaps when this enterprise was ongoing and all the smoke and dirt from the fires and coal dust that was flying about, then maybe the American could be forgiven for concluding his visit here with an amusing observation of the workers by saying that: "The people with their black and rough cheeks did not add to the appearance of the place."

This part of the ironworks was not built until 1839, but when complete, at the top of this tower would have stood a water balance wheel. The water balance was used to raise full trams of material from floor level to the top of the tower, so any products for the furnace charge could be lifted to a level where they could be fed into the furnaces, while among its other duties the lift could be used so that trams of pig iron could be drawn by horse along the tramway to the forge at Garndyris, where they processed the pig iron into wrought iron that was destined for many different parts of the world. After meandering the Blorenge mountain, the trams of wrought iron arrived at the canal wharf in Llanfoist where the iron was transferred onto barges that were mainly en route to Newport docks by way of the Brecknock and Abergavenny canal.

As an example of local iron being produced at the time of the building of this water balance lift, the amount being sent to Newport on the canal in 1838 by the Blaenavon and Garndyris Company was 12,427 tons, British Iron Company, 12,482 tons; Pentwyn and Golynos Company, 12,535 tons; Varteg iron works, 12,820 tons and C.H. Leigh Pontypool, 8,047 tons but the total amount of iron transported to Newport by canal for Monmouthshire in that year was 167,478 tons.

Index

Index